THE OPEN UNIVERSITY   A SCIENCE FOUNDATION C

G000136792

UNITS 5–6 INTO THE EAR
EARTHQUAKES, SEISMOLOGY AND THE
EARTH'S MAGNETISM

THE SCIENCE FOUNDATION COURSE TEAM

Steve Best (Illustrator)
Geoff Brown (Earth Sciences)
Jim Burge (BBC)
Neil Chalmers (Biology)
Bob Cordell (Biology, General Editor)
Pauline Corfield (Assessment Group and
    Summer School Group)
Debbie Crouch (Designer)
Dee Edwards (Earth Sciences; S101 Evaluation)
Graham Farmelo (Chairman)
John Greenwood (Librarian)
Mike Gunton (BBC)
Charles Harding (Chemistry)
Robin Harding (Biology)
Nigel Harris (Earth Sciences, General Editor)
Linda Hodgkinson (Course Coordinator)
David Jackson (BBC)
David Johnson (Chemistry, General Editor)
Tony Jolly (BBC, Series Producer)
Ken Kirby (BBC)
Perry Morley (Editor)
Peter Morrod (Chemistry)
Pam Owen (Illustrator)
Rissa de la Paz (BBC)
Julia Powell (Editor)
David Roberts (Chemistry)
David Robinson (Biology)
Shelagh Ross (Physics, General Editor)
Dick Sharp (Editor)

Ted Smith (BBC)
Margaret Swithenby (Editor)
Nick Watson (BBC)
Dave Williams (Earth Sciences)
Geoff Yarwood (Earth Sciences)

Consultants:
Keith Hodgkinson (Physics)
Judith Metcalfe (Biology)
Pat Murphy (Biology)
Irene Ridge (Biology)
Jonathan Silvertown (Biology)

External assessor: F. J. Vine FRS

Others whose S101 contribution has been of
considerable value in the preparation of S102:

Stuart Freake (Physics)
Anna Furth (Biology)
Stephen Hurry (Biology)
Jane Nelson (Chemistry)
Mike Pentz (Chairman and General Editor, S101)
Milo Shott (Physics)
Russell Stannard (Physics)
Steve Swithenby (Physics)
Peggy Varley (Biology)
Kiki Warr (Chemistry)
Chris Wilson (Earth Sciences)

The drawing on the front cover is from Copernicus's original manuscript, and places the Sun at the centre of the Universe.

The Open University, Walton Hall, Milton Keynes, MK7 6AA.

First Published 1987, Reprinted 1989, 1990.

Designed by the Graphic Design Group of the Open University.

Filmset by Santype International Limited, Salisbury, Wiltshire; printed by Thomson Litho, East Kilbride, Scotland.

ISBN 0 335 16327 0

This text forms part of an Open University Course. For general availability of supporting material referred to in this text please write to: Open University Educational Enterprises Limited, 12 Cofferidge Close, Stony Stratford, Milton Keynes, MK11 1BY, Great Britain.

Further information on Open University Courses may be obtained from the Admissions Office, The Open University, P.O. Box 48, Walton Hall, Milton Keynes, MK7 6AB.

1.3

'A bad earthquake at once destroys the oldest associations; the world, the very emblem of all that is solid, had moved beneath our feet like a crust over a fluid; one second of time has created in the mind a strong idea of insecurity, which hours of reflection would not have produced'.

(Charles Darwin—reflecting on his feeling the devastating 20 February 1835 earthquake in Concepcion, Chile)

STUDY GUIDE

Units 5–8 are concerned with an area of science that may be new to you–Earth sciences. They are presented as two double Units: Units 5–6, which are about 'whole Earth' topics that follow from your study of the Earth as a planet in Units 1 and 2; and Units 7–8 which focus on the outer parts of the solid Earth, and their behaviour. This, the first double Unit has six main Sections, and you should aim to reach the end of Section 3 by the end of the first week.

Near the beginning of Section 1, you will be asked to work through the first AV sequence (which should take about 20 minutes) and for this you will need the rock samples and hand lens from your Experiment Kit and a rule. There are a number of Colour Plates at the back of this double Unit which you will need to refer to, particularly when working through the AV sequences.

In Section 3, you will be asked to carry out a few simple experiments using the following items from the Kit: bar magnets, compass and iron filings. You will also need a sheet of plain A4 paper, a pair of compasses (with which to draw a circle) and two books each about 1 cm thick (or something similar, such as pieces of plywood). These experiments will take altogether about an hour to complete.

The first of the two TV programmes associated with Units 5–6, entitled 'Earthquakes—seismology at work', can be watched with benefit at any point during the week as it is relevant to all of Sections 1–3.

Towards the end of Section 4, there is another AV sequence, which should take about 40 minutes to work through; again, you will be using the rock samples and hand lens from the Kit and referring to the Colour Plates at the back of the text.

The second TV programme for this double Unit, called 'Magnetic Earth', is especially relevant to Sections 3 and 5.

Although we have mentioned the Sections in which you will make most use of the rock samples we have sent you, if possible try to have them to hand during the whole of your study of Units 5–8. We will frequently mention the rocks by name and the more you see and handle them, the more familiar you will become with their features and properties. If you can, fix the World Ocean Floor map (in Part 1 of the Kit) on the wall near your place of study; you can then readily refer to the places and features as they are mentioned during these Units. Please note that as *the map is a returnable Kit item*, you should not write on it, or mark it in any other way.

We hope you enjoy your introduction to Earth sciences.

I AN INTRODUCTION TO EARTH SCIENCES

The article opposite, which appeared in *The Guardian* on 20 September 1985, concerns one of the worst natural disasters this century, an earthquake which in just two minutes devastated much of Mexico City (Figure 1). Although the article has some terms in it which may be unfamiliar to

FIGURE 1 Collapsed multi-storey building following the 1985 earthquake in Mexico City.

you, it should nevertheless bring home to you one of the reasons why we study earthquakes—to learn how to avert such major human disasters. But there are plenty of side-benefits for understanding the Earth, as you will soon find out!

But why did the earthquake occur in that place and at that time? Could it have been predicted? Why do most earthquakes occur only in certain regions of the Earth? Questions like these are the concern of **Earth sciences,** the scientific study of the interior and surface of the Earth.

I.I THE ORIGINS OF EARTH SCIENCES

The study of Earth sciences is relatively young compared with, say, chemistry which has its origins in alchemy during the Middle Ages, or physics which was practised in a crude form in Ancient Greece. The first geologists were associated with practical projects, in which it was found that a knowledge of the underlying rocks and their properties was important; for example William Smith (1769–1839), one of the founders of British geology, was involved in the surveying and digging of the canal system in England.

A major aspect of Smith's work was the discovery that particular groups of **fossils** (the remains of animal and plant life) were found together in rock beds and that the fossil groups were quite distinct from those in beds above and below. This led to his correlation work and the discovery that rocks get younger towards the south-east of England. He paved the way for the study of two branches of geology which you will meet in Units 28–29: stratigraphy (the study of rock formations) and palaeontology (the study of fossils).

The development of Britain's coalfields was also dependent upon a knowledge of geology; starting from where coal could be found at the surface, an understanding of the sequences of rock layers in which coal is located led to the prediction of underground seams. In this century, Earth scientists have played a crucial role in the location of oil and gas, in such inhospitable places as the North Sea, northern Alaska and the deserts of the Middle East. There are many other examples of the applications of the Earth

Mexico City bears the brunt as three states are engulfed

Thousand feared killed in quake

From Michael White in Washington

Up to 1,000 people were feared dead last night and hundreds more injured in the rubble of fallen buildings in Mexico City after an earthquake engulfed three Mexican states and shook buildings as far away as Texas.

In sparsely-populated coastal states, a church collapsed during a mass killing 25 people and ancient cathedrals were also reportedly destroyed. The brunt of the earthquake, measuring 7.8 on the Richter scale, was borne by the Mexican capital, a vast congested city of 18 million people, caught during the morning rush hour.

President Miguel de la Madrid declared the city a disaster area. Some reports put the death toll at up to 1,000 — others at between 150 and 300 — and said that as many as 35 per cent of the city's buildings were damaged.

One television station continued to operate in the chaos and transmitted pictures to the outside world while all other communications and air links were thrown into confusion. The goverment-owned Channel 13 showed old and new buildings in rubble, dense smoke and fire in some of the city's most fashionable areas—including tourist hotels reportedly damaged —and rescue workers looking frantically for bodies in the ruins.

Troops were brought in and the Government appealed for help overseas. Civilians were asked to donate petrol to the military as supplies ran short. Hospitals, some already damaged, filled rapidly. One radio ham operator, a main source of information in the confusion, said: "I felt only one earthquake, but it was terribly long. I've never felt one like this before. I saw a lot of dead and trapped."

Some accounts spoke of up to 2,000 people being trapped in a collapsed building and of a building as high as 13 storeys being destroyed. A seven-storey radio station "collapsed like a sandcastle," said one witness, and a tourist motel was destroyed.

Mexican embassy officials in Washington identified the central areas of Colonia Roma and Colonia Doctores as the most seriously damaged parts of the city. Television pictures showed a severely damaged hotel near the central Monument of the Revolution. Ham radio operators reported people seeing many dead in the streets and doctors had taken patients "out into the street because they thought it was safer".

The epicentre of the earthquake was thought to be about 40 miles offshore in the Pacific Ocean, 150 miles north-west of Acapulco. No word emerged early today from the popular resort, the city closest to the epicentre, increasing fears that it too had sustained major damage.

Electricity and gas lines were disrupted, fires added to rescuers' problems in the capital and Mexico City airport remained closed. Questions were being asked about the scandals surrounding the abuse of building regulations in Mexico, which may have led to the collapse of hotels, flats and office buildings.

There were reports of buildings shaking and water splashing out of swimming pools in Houston and Corpus Christi in south-east Texas, almost 1,000 miles away. Mexico's worst earthquake of recent times was in September, 1973 when one measuring 6.5 — over 7 ranks as a major disturbance—killed more than 700 people.

In March another registering 7.8 on the Richter scale killed 177 people in Chile, a part of the perpetual movement along the great Pacific fault line which destroyed San Francisco in 1906.

Estimates of the death toll varied enormously in the confusion. Cautious estimates rose gradually from 150 to 250 and 300 with predictions on Mexican television that the tally would reach 1,000.

Survivors in coastal areas said that a US weather station in Honolulu had issued a related tidal wave warning for Central America, from California to Ecuador, and were unaware that the warning was later cancelled.

Spain's Prime Minister, Mr Felipe Gonzalez, said that his Government was coordinating a flight with the Spanish Red Cross to fly medicine, tents and blankets to Mexico.

sciences, such as the location of mineral deposits, from copper and gold to more mundane but essential commodities such as iron ore for steel, limestone for cement and gravel for the construction industry.

1.2 EARTH SCIENCES: SCOPE AND METHODS

'Earth sciences' and 'geology' are often used synonymously but the former is the broader term because it includes the study of the oceans and the atmosphere as well as the solid Earth. It also implies an *integrated* approach to the various 'sub-disciplines' which the study of Earth sciences embraces (for example, geophysics and geochemistry), rather than the pursuit of one compartmentalized specialist area of science.

Like many of the branches of modern science the study of the Earth is essentially an *observational* science. Geologists, for example, study rocks in the field and laboratory and often make maps or plot their data diagrammatically; it is this observational basis which helps them to develop hypotheses about the processes that led to the formation and subsequent evolution of rocks. If an hypothesis stands up to repeated testing in other suitable geological situations it may be raised to the status of a *theory*. It is worth noting that theories in biology and Earth sciences often do not resemble those in physics and chemistry which are usually expressed in equations and symbols. Theory in Earth sciences is usually more qualitative and expressed in words. Fieldwork studies continue to play an important part in the development of the subject, but in order to extend the human perspective we rely increasingly on sophisticated technology, using microscopes and satellites.

RELIEF

MAGMA

Telescopes and cameras have been placed in satellites which orbit the Earth (see Plate 1, at the end of the text) and in others sent out of Earth orbit, for example in the *Voyager* missions to visit the outer planets, from where instrumental observations are sent back for analysis. This branch of science is called *remote sensing* and leads some to suggest that the discipline name should be extended to 'Earth and planetary sciences'. You may have seen photographs of the surface of Mars, or the tail of Halley's comet, or the moons of Jupiter, Saturn and Uranus, from which Earth scientists have made deductions about the surface geology, composition and history of these bodies.

☐ What factors restrict direct observation of the rocks at the Earth's surface?

■ The oceans cover about two-thirds of the globe (see the World Ocean Floor map) and this makes direct observation of the Earth's surface in oceanic areas very difficult. Also soil, permanent ice cover and vegetation, such as tropical forest, hamper observation on land.

Satellite photographs of the Earth's surface can help with the geological interpretation of an area, and they can be particularly valuable when dealing with inaccessible areas, especially where bare rock is exposed. But overall only a very small part of the Earth's surface can be observed directly. The most important point, however, is that even in the deepest mines we hardly scratch the surface of the *whole* Earth, and it is the Earth's interior that is our main concern in this double Unit.

First, to get a feel for the scale of the surface undulations, or **relief** of the Earth, answer the following ITQ.

ITQ 1   The highest points above sea-level on the Earth's surface lie in the Himalayas, at about 8 850 m above sea-level. The lowest point below sea-level is the Mariana Trench, which you can find on the World Ocean Floor map at 140° E, 10–20° N, i.e. between New Guinea and Japan. The depth below sea-level here is about 11 000 m. The radius of the Earth is 6 370 km.*

(a) What is the ratio of the total relief (the difference between the Earth's lowest and highest point) to the radius of the Earth? What is this ratio as a percentage?

(b) Now imagine that you were to draw a circle of radius 5 cm (to represent the Earth) using a sharp pencil, which produces a line width of, say, 0.2 mm. How does the thickness of the line compare with the total relief, if this were drawn to scale?

As the deepest mines for metals or coal penetrate to a few kilometres, only through some of the deepest boreholes yet drilled have we beaten nature's depth recorded in the Mariana Trench.

Now, as we are interested in the *interior* of the Earth, it should be clear to you that most of our knowledge cannot have come from direct observation; instead we rely on various kinds of *indirect* methods. Natural phenomena such as volcanoes, earthquakes and the Earth's magnetism can tell us a good deal about the composition and structure of the interior of the Earth and after reading this double Unit we hope that you will understand and be able to interpret some of this evidence. Other geological processes have brought rocks to the surface from depths of up to 300 km, but this still leaves a depth of about 6 000 km totally unsampled.

These direct observations and indirect methods are used together to develop *models* of the Earth's interior composition and structure.

handwritten: 3.11×10^{-3}
handwritten: $3.11 \times 10^{-4}\%$
handwritten: 0.1%

* As explained later (in Section 1.3), this is the average radius of the Earth. (In Unit 2 we used a value of 6 380 km, which is the radius of the Earth at the Equator.)

You first met modelling in Unit 1, where you considered the pancake and spherical models of the Earth, and the geocentric and heliocentric models for the relationship between the Earth and the Sun. As you will recall, scientific models are not scaled-down replicas of objects, but are ways of representing relationships between the *characteristics* of real objects, or systems of objects.

For example, the law of gravitation, discussed in Unit 3, can be used to derive a *mathematical model* for the shape of the Earth's orbit. As another example, the economy of the country can be modelled by representing people and industries as parameters in equations. *Diagrammatic models*, such as those used in architectural scale drawings and plans, are also useful in science (as you will see in Figure 2). It is by combining the attributes of various different modelling techniques that we can often obtain a better understanding of the phenomena being studied. Having prepared a model, the next logical step is to test it by using it to make predictions about the behaviour of the modelled system, either observed directly or through experiment. The model may then be modified and refined in the light of these observations. Much of the later Sections of this double Unit will be about the refinement of two simple models for the Earth, using the interpretation of earthquake data and other information. One will be a physical model, representing the internal structure of the Earth, and the other will be a chemical model, representing the Earth's composition.

1.3 WHAT DO WE KNOW ABOUT THE EARTH?

1.3.1 SIZE, SHAPE AND INTERNAL TEMPERATURE OF THE EARTH

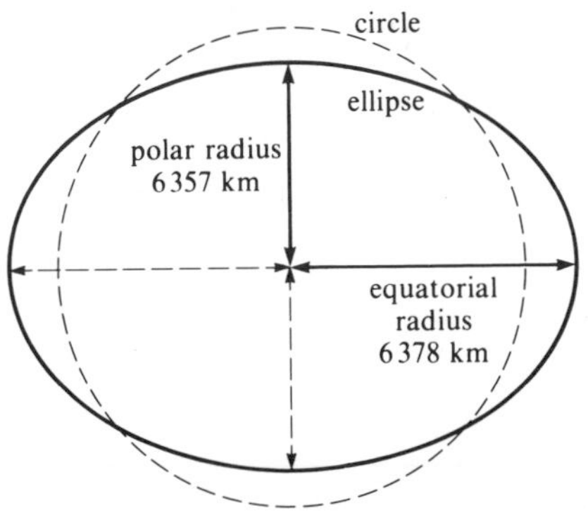

Studies of eclipses and satellite photographs (Plate 1) show that the Earth is nearly spherical. In fact, the average equatorial radius is 6 378 km, compared with the average polar radius of 6 357 km, and this is shown (as a diagrammatic model) in a highly exaggerated way in Figure 2. The difference in the radii, 21 km, is about 0.3% of the radius which, if drawn to scale, would be lost in the thickness of the printed line (see ITQ 1). However, the bulge is sufficient to rob the Himalayas of the honour of having the point on the Earth's surface furthest from its centre. This distinction goes to the peak of a volcano in equatorial South America!

The reason why the Earth has an equatorial bulge is connected with its spin about its axis of rotation. When an object spins, material is moved outwards in a direction perpendicular to the axis but, as we know, the Earth is rigid enough to maintain a stable shape which is a close approximation to a sphere.

We can also surmise that at least parts of the interior of the Earth are hot.

☐ What sort of evidence for the Earth's interior heat do you know about?

■ Active volcanic areas, such as Hawaii in the Pacific Ocean, Stromboli in the Mediterranean, Iceland and the Azores in the Atlantic, show evidence that hot molten rock material is close to the Earth's surface in these places. This molten rock is called **magma**, and where it is erupted at the Earth's surface, a volcano will be produced.

It is also known that the temperature rises in deep mines, and this can make the working conditions at depth extremely unpleasant.

☐ If the temperature rises by 2 °C for every 100 m (0.1 km), what is the temperature at 1 km depth, assuming that the surface temperature is 10 °C?

■ 30 °C; 10 °C surface temperature +20 °C for 1 km depth.

FIGURE 2 A diagrammatic representation of the Earth, showing the equatorial bulge and polar flattening (greatly exaggerated).

$$\frac{1000}{2} \times \frac{100}{100} \; km = 50 \; km$$

ITQ 2 Assuming that, on average, temperature rises at a constant rate of 2 °C per 100 m depth and that the lowest temperature at which a volcanic rock can be molten is about 1 000 °C, how far do you have to go down into the Earth to reach this temperature? (You may ignore the surface temperature in your calculation.)

So, if the assumptions in ITQ 2 are true, although we find molten volcanic rock at the surface where the normal temperature range is 0–50 °C, the temperature of molten rock means that most volcanoes must have their sources at considerable depths. In fact, it has been found that the rates at which the temperature rises with depth into the Earth vary over the Earth, so the situation is not as simple as ITQ 2 implies, but it's a useful first approximation.

1.3.2 ROCKS AND ROCK TEXTURES (AV SEQUENCE)

So far, we have been talking about the Earth in a rather abstract way and before we start to probe the inaccessible interior, it's time to introduce you to some Earth materials. Although the small selection of rocks we have sent you represents only some of the rocks present in the outermost skin of the Earth, they will help to give you a feel for what the Earth is made of, so we would like you to take a brief look at them at this stage. Later on (Section 4.5) you will be introduced to a systematic examination of the rock samples, but during Sections 2 and 3 we will make direct reference to some types of rock, so we would like you to have a preliminary look at them now.

Before starting the AV sequence, get out the rock samples and hand lens from the Kit and set up a good source of light (Figure 3). You will find the AV sequence on Tape 1 (Side 2, Band 1). This begins by explaining how to examine rocks using the hand lens. The main part of the AV sequence is concerned with identifying *rock textures*, by the size of the particles making up the rock and their relationships to each other. Work through this AV sequence, stopping the tape to fill in the blanks in Table 1 as you go along.

Terms in AV sequence:

SEDIMENTARY ROCKS

IGNEOUS ROCKS

TEXTURE OF A ROCK

FRAGMENTAL TEXTURE

QUARTZ

SANDSTONE

MUDSTONE

CEMENT

LIMESTONE

GRANITE

GLASSY TEXTURE

CRYSTALLINE TEXTURE

INTRUSIVE

EROSION

BASALT

VESICULAR (FROTHY) BASALT

LAVA

LAVA FLOW

EFFUSIVE

EXTRUSIVE

PERIDOTITE

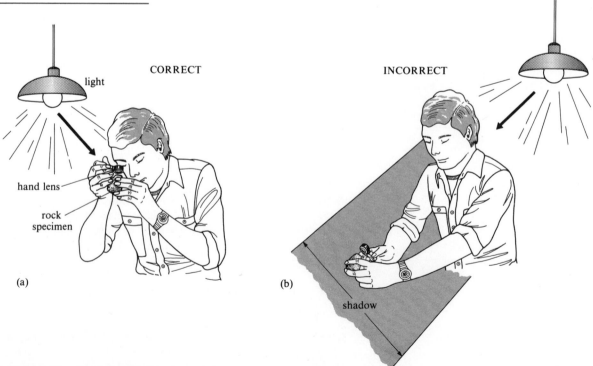

FIGURE 3 (a) The correct way to use a hand lens: the lens is held 2–3 cm from the eye and the rock sample is held a further 5 cm or so from the lens; (b) incorrect use of a hand lens. Note also that the light should be to one side, not behind.

TABLE 1 The examination of rock hand specimens (for use with AV sequence)

	Specimen	Description	Formation
SEDIMENTARY ROCKS	S6 SANDSTONE Plate *5*	Texture FRAGMENTAL Grain size: 1–2 mm, clearly visible Mineral(s) *quartz*	Plate *3*
	Mudstone (no specimen)	Fine-grained	Plate *7*
	S7 *L/stone*	Notable feature FOSSIL FRAGMENTS	Plate *9*
IGNEOUS ROCKS	S1 *Intrusive* Plate *9*	Texture *Crystalline* Minerals and grain sizes *coarse grained* *10 – 2 mm*	Plate *12*
	S2 *Basalt*	Texture *Interlocking Crystalline fine grained*	Plate *11*
	S3 *Basalt*	Texture *Interlocking Crystalline* Grain size *FINE*	Plate *12*
	S4 *Peridotite* Plate *13*	Texture *Interlocking Crystalline* Grain size *½ – 1 mm*	(no Plate)

9

PRESSURE

CRUST

1.3.3 THE DENSITY OF THE EARTH'S INTERIOR

The rocks you have just looked at play an important part in understanding the Earth's interior, but before we set up the model of the Earth's structure there is one more aspect to consider. What do you think happens to the *density* of rocks as we go down into the Earth? Let's start by considering a situation closer to home: the accumulation of snow. Powdery snow collects in hollows in mountainous areas and, if it gets deep enough, the pressure of the overlying snow is so great that the snow at the bottom is crushed to a more consolidated form and may be changed to ice. (If the pressure is great enough the solid ice starts to *flow* as a glacier.) The snow becomes denser with increasing depth as the particles are compacted by the removal of air. The density of snow is about one-tenth that of water (powdery snow occupies ten times the volume of an equivalent mass of water) and the density of ice is about nine-tenths that of water (which is why ice floats), so in changing from snow to ice, the density increases about ninefold.

As discussed above, powdery snow may be changed into ice by the pressure of the overlying snow. Now **pressure** is defined as follows:

$$\text{pressure} = \frac{\text{perpendicular force}}{\text{area}} \qquad (1)$$

In SI units, pressure is measured in newtons per square metre (N m^{-2}). As with the snow–ice analogy, at any given depth inside the Earth, the weight of the overlying rocks (i.e. their perpendicular, downwards-directed force) will exert pressure on the rocks below. Imagine a horizontal area A at a particular depth which we shall call h (Figure 4). The *volume* of rock above this area must therefore be Ah. We know the expression that relates the *weight* of the rock to its *mass* (see Unit 3, Section 4.3):

weight = mass × acceleration due to gravity

= volume × density × acceleration due to gravity

Substituting Ah for the volume, we get:

weight = $Ah\rho g$

where density is denoted by the Greek letter ρ (rho) and g is the acceleration due to gravity.*

Therefore, using Equation 1:

$$\text{pressure} = \frac{\text{perpendicular force (weight)}}{\text{area}} = \frac{Ah\rho g}{A}$$

$$= h\rho g \qquad (\text{SI units: } \text{N m}^{-2}) \qquad (2)$$

In words, this tells us that pressure is depth times density times acceleration due to gravity.

To get some idea of the pressures that are exerted on rocks within the Earth, answer the following ITQ.

ITQ 3 If the average density of the Earth is $5.5 \times 10^3 \text{ kg m}^{-3}$ and the acceleration due to gravity g is 10 m s^{-2}, what is the pressure at a depth of 100 km?

So the pressure at a depth of 100 km inside the Earth is more than four orders of magnitude greater than normal atmospheric pressure at the Earth's surface. Imagine a column of some 50 million apples stacked one on top of the other. If the cross-sectional area of this hypothetical column was about 0.01 m^2, then the pressure on the bottom apple would be equal

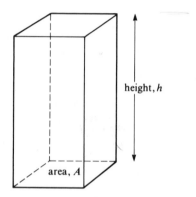

FIGURE 4 Volume = Ah.

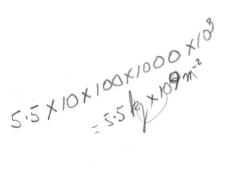

---

* In Unit 3 we used the symbol g_E to denote the acceleration due to gravity towards the Earth, but here and in subsequent Units we use just g.

to that at 100 km depth inside the Earth. More realistically, when the weight of half a million tonnes of rock is applied to every square metre at 100 km depth, the effects on rocks down there must be severe, to say the least. We think that similar sorts of processes to those described in the snow and ice analogy apply to the whole Earth. For example, water and air are expelled during the transformation of beach sand into a sand*stone* at depths of a few tens to a few hundreds of metres. At greater depths, rocks become much more dense because of the increasing weight of the overlying material, and this has important implications for the variation of density with depth inside the Earth.

First let us consider the rock samples provided in the Kit, each of which has a density between 2.5×10^3 and $3.5 \times 10^3 \, \mathrm{kg \, m^{-3}}$. In Unit 3 we worked out a value of $5.6 \times 10^3 \, \mathrm{kg \, m^{-3}}$ for the density of the whole Earth, which is close to the accepted value of $5.5 \times 10^3 \, \mathrm{kg \, m^{-3}}$. It is clear that rocks towards the centre of the Earth must be more dense than $5.5 \times 10^3 \, \mathrm{kg \, m^{-3}}$ in order to compensate for the lower density of the rocks close to the surface. This is an extremely important observation to which we shall return later on. You will see in subsequent Sections that we can identify a number of shell-like layers within the Earth in which density increases progressively towards the centre.

1.4 A SIMPLE MODEL OF THE STRUCTURE OF THE EARTH

We are now going to describe a simple model of the structure of the Earth which you should bear in mind as you read on; the reasoning behind the model and the evidence that enables us to learn more about the interior will be presented later in this double Unit. The structure of the Earth's interior is illustrated in Figure 5.

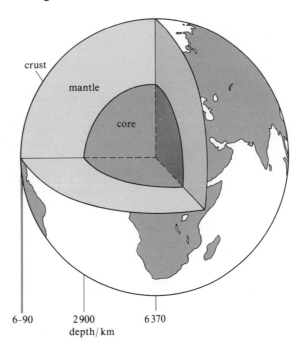

FIGURE 5   A simple model of the internal structure of the Earth.

The Earth has an outer skin called the **crust** and most of the rock samples we have sent you come from this layer. The Earth's crust varies in thickness, from about 6 km at its thinnest, to about 90 km at its thickest and is, on average, 35 km deep. But on the scale of the whole Earth (radius about 6 370 km) this is very small, so the crust is relatively very thin. As you know from looking at the world around you, most of the top of the crust is fairly rigid and cold (for a rock 50 °C—the maximum temperature of the Earth's surface—is cold, and the places where molten rocks reach the surface are few in number). When crustal rocks (i.e. the rocks comprising the Earth's crust) are subjected to strong and long-lasting forces, or when they are warm, rock beds may bend and crumple; this is called **folding** (Figure 6).

FIGURE 6   Folds in rock beds at Stair Hole, Lulworth Cove, Dorset. The scale is indicated by the silhouette of a figure on the cliff top.

But when pressures are exerted over short time-scales, rock beds may fracture and break; you will have met behaviour like this when breaking a bar of cold toffee, or the substance 'silly putty'. We use phrases like 'solid as a rock' and we know that the quarrying of stone often requires dynamite; however, your study of Earth sciences will lead you to see that the Earth is not quite as solid as you might think.

Below the crust is a very thick, denser layer, which occupies nearly 70% of the Earth's volume and is called the **mantle**. The mantle itself is subdivided into a number of shells which we shall describe later. In the centre of the Earth there is a **core**, which is even denser and, we believe, metallic rather than rocky. In part this accounts for the increase in density towards the centre of the Earth. Another important factor is that the Earth's magnetic field appears to originate within the core; consequently the study of the Earth's magnetism (Section 3) provides information about the core and its properties.

It might help you to get a feel for the internal structure of the Earth by thinking of it as a spherical, unripe avocado pear. In this model, **the spherical avocado pear model**, the thin skin of the avocado pear represents the crust, the flesh represents the mantle, and the large, hard stone at the centre represents the core. Interpreting the structure of the Earth is like trying to find out what's inside the avocado pear by only scratching the skin. How can you tell how big the central stone is?

We can now return to the subject of earthquakes. Energy from earthquakes passes through the Earth, so earthquake behaviour provides us with a kind of 'X-ray' technique for building up a picture of the internal structure of our planet.

THE EARTHQUAKE.

TO THE EDITOR OF THE TIMES.

Sir,—As you may think any accurate observation of the shock of earthquake which was felt in various parts of England last Tuesday morning worth publishing I send you mine.

I was awakened by a violent swaying of my bedstead from side to side, accompanied by a singular heaving motion. It was exactly as if some great beast had been crouching asleep under the bedstead and were now shaking itself and trying to rise. The time by my watch was 20 minutes past 3, and I suppose the shock to have lasted nearly a minute. The bedstead, a large iron one, standing nearly north and south, appeared to me to be the only piece of furniture in the room that was heavily shaken. Neither the doors nor the windows rattled, though they rattle enough in windy weather, this house standing alone, on high ground, in the neighbourhood of two great rivers. There was no noise. The air was very still, and much warmer than it had been in the earlier part of the night. Although the previous afternoon had been wet, the glass had not fallen. I had mentioned my surprise at its standing near the letter "i" in "Fair," and having a tendency to rise. It is recorded in the second volume of the *Philosophical Transactions* that the glass stood high at Oxford when an earthquake was felt there in September, 1683. Your faithful servant,

CHARLES DICKENS.

Gad's-hill-place, Higham by Rochester, Kent, Oct. 7.

1.5 WHAT HAPPENS DURING AN EARTHQUAKE?

The effect of heavy traffic passing close to a building is often felt as ground vibrations by the occupants. This illustrates the passage of sound energy through rocks in much the same way as, on a larger scale, the energy of earthquakes can be transmitted over greater distances. Although no catastrophic earthquakes have ever occurred in Britain, minor tremors have often been observed, for example that documented by Charles Dickens in his letter to *The Times* in October 1863 (see margin). In recent times, several small earthquakes have occurred; for example, at Carlisle in 1979 and in north Wales in both 1984 and 1986.

In stronger earthquakes, observers tell of very loud noise, like thunder, accompanying movement of the ground. This movement may take different forms, from very rapid vibrations of small size, to a slower but greater rise and fall of the land; height oscillations of 0.5 m over a few seconds have been observed during earthquakes. As a result, buildings can crack and topple, railway tracks and fences can be buckled and road surfaces broken; dams can break and lose their water catastrophically, landslides can be triggered which destroy roads and villages, and bridges can be swept away. Frequently the secondary effects resulting from an earthquake, such as landslides, are more serious than the earthquake itself. Some interesting examples of earthquake effects are shown in Figures 7 and 8 and in the TV programme 'Earthquakes—seismology at work'.

If an earthquake originates under an ocean, waves can be sent across the water which increase in size as the water shallows near the shore. These **tsunamis** are often called 'tidal waves', though this is not really correct as they have nothing to do with normal tides (which are generated through the gravitational attraction between the Earth and the Moon and Sun). In low-lying coastal areas, tsunamis are some of the most destructive and life-threatening of an earthquake's effects, especially as hundreds or thousands of kilometres away from the earthquake, the population may not be prepared for the approaching waves, which may be up to 20 m high. An earth-

FIGURE 8   A broken road stripe in Montana, USA, following an earthquake in August 1959.

FIGURE 7   Fourth Avenue, Anchorage, Alaska after the earthquake on Good Friday 1964. The north side (on the left of the photograph) has dropped relative to the south side, which is comparatively undamaged. Schools and shops were almost empty because of the public holiday and consequently there were fewer casualties than might have occurred on a normal weekday.

FIGURE 9 Foundation failure as a result of ground liquefaction caused these buildings in Japan to topple intact; the building fabric withstood the earthquake but the underlying geology did not. (Niagara earthquake, offshore epicentre near Honshu Island, June 1964)

FIGURE 10 The focus is the site of initial slip on the fault. The epicentre is the point on the surface vertically above the focus. Zones of earthquake intensity on the Mercalli scale are indicated by I to IV—the intensity decreases as distance from the focus increases.

quake in Chile in 1960 caused a series of waves, each preceded by the sea withdrawing: the third and fourth waves were the highest. Loss of life occurred largely because people returned to watch the sea recede the second time, not realizing that a 7 m high wave was advancing towards the coast. This tsunami travelled across the Pacific Ocean at a speed of about $180 \, \text{m s}^{-1}$ (650 km per hour): 22 hours after the earthquake, the tsunami reached the Japanese coast and caused \$70 million worth of damage.

The **intensity of an earthquake**, as measured in terms of visible damage and devastation caused to buildings, can be assessed on the **Mercalli scale.** This is a purely *observational* (and thus rather subjective) scale on which earthquakes labelled I–VI are 'minor', VI–VIII are 'damaging', VIII–X are 'destructive' and X–XII 'major' or 'great'.

☐ Can you think of reasons why, when dealing with buildings, it is difficult to compile a meaningful scale of damage?

■ Damage to buildings depends on several factors, for example the method of construction (timber-framed buildings withstand greater shocks than concrete or brick ones) and the nature of the foundations. Buildings on large 'rafts' of concrete survive better than ones with less substantial foundations.

The nature of the underlying rocks is an important factor in determining the severity of earthquake damage as softer materials, such as sands and clays, can liquefy during an earthquake so that even buildings of an earthquake-resistant fabric can topple whole (Figure 9).

But why do earthquakes take place? What causes apparently rigid rocks to buckle and fracture? The answer is that the Earth is an extremely mobile or dynamic place when looked at on a geological time-scale of many millions of years. As you will find in Units 7–8, large-scale movement of material within the Earth causes the build-up of lateral pressure in the rocks, until this eventually exceeds the rock's breaking point. The rock then fractures, releasing energy. The line of fracture is called a **fault**; the place at which the first movement on the fault occurs is where the earthquake originates and is called the **focus**; and the point on the Earth's surface directly above the focus is called the **epicentre** (Figure 10). Generally speaking, with increasing

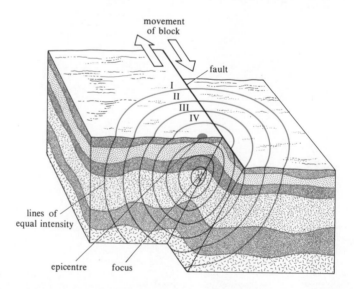

distance from the focus, there are zones of decreasing damage, which can be described in terms of decreasing earthquake intensity. Once a fracture or fault has moved, generating an earthquake, pressure can build up again until the force of friction between the rocks on each side of the fault is overcome and the fault will move again.

Natural faults and the movements with which they are associated can be classified into three main groups (Figure 11). The movement may be mainly vertical as in Figures 11a and 11b: in (a) there has been a pull-apart or

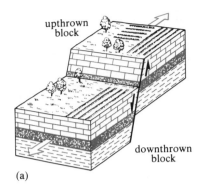

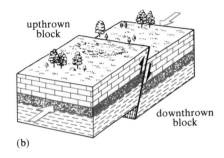

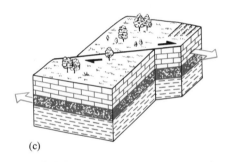

FIGURE 11 Types of faulting: (a) due to stretching with mainly vertical motion, (b) due to compression with mainly vertical motion, and (c) due to shearing where the blocks slide past each other. The red arrows denote the direction of the forces acting on the blocks, and the black arrows the direction of movement.

stretching motion whereas (b) shows the result of compression. In contrast, the movement may be mainly horizontal, as in Figure 11c which illustrates a shearing motion in which the adjacent blocks slide past each other. The example shown in Figure 7 is a vertical fault whereas that in Figure 8 is a horizontal fault. Faults can occur at all scales from, say, 2 cm displacements which might be seen by close examination of rocks exposed in a road cutting, to faults on a continental scale that can be seen easily only in satellite photographs. Movement of a fault during earthquakes can be a few centimetres to several metres.

ITQ 4 Look at Plates 2a and 2b, which are aerial photographs; what evidence can you see of faulting in these photographs? Draw a sketch of the main features of Plate 2b, indicating what you think is the position of the fault and the relative direction of movement.

Plates 2a and 2b show part of a famous fault in California, called the San Andreas Fault, where the major movement is horizontal and has been continuing for millions of years. This fault has been the source of many, frequently large, earthquakes, including one in 1906 that resulted in the destruction of San Francisco from fire, following the rupture of gas mains; the water mains were also ruptured, so there was no effective fire-fighting equipment available. During this earthquake, the land to the west of the San Andreas Fault moved 6.5 m relative to the other side and it was the identification of the displacement, visible along several hundred kilometres of this fault, that brought the realization that faults and earthquakes are connected. The area that ruptured during this earthquake was 400 km long and, it is believed, 15 km deep. A simplified map of southern California showing the major parts of the fault system (as several related faults are involved) is shown in Figure 12. As indicated by the red arrows in the Figure, the area south and west of the fault is moving towards the north and north-west.

California has the largest population of all States in the USA and is the centre of many 'high tech' industries. In fact, there are several towns and nuclear power stations situated near the San Andreas Fault, which also passes close to the University of California (Berkeley), Stanford University, and the western headquarters of the US Geological Survey! Earthquakes are, therefore, a very serious subject for Californians, and we shall return to this topic at the end of this double Unit.

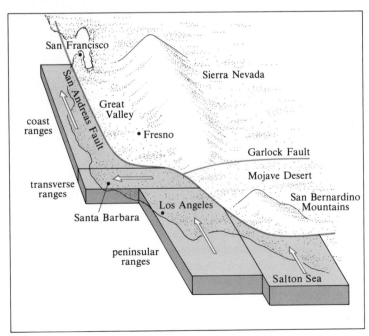

FIGURE 12 A simplified map of the San Andreas Fault System (SAFS) in California, showing the direction of movement of the Earth's crust.

1.6 WHERE DO EARTHQUAKES OCCUR?

Earthquakes happen continually; it has been estimated that one million occur in any year, but obviously these are not all major events. However, during the drafting of this Section in late 1986, there was a large earthquake in San Salvador, involving great loss of life and within a few months or years of reading these Units you will hear of other earthquake disasters. Figure 13 shows the distribution of large earthquakes over a recent time interval; it is very important that you examine this Figure carefully in conjunction with the World Ocean Floor map.

ITQ 5 (a) Briefly (in a few sentences) describe the pattern of earthquake distribution shown in Figure 13 (using the geographical names on the World Ocean Floor map).

(b) What sorts of features shown on the World Ocean Floor map appear to be correlated with the positions of the epicentres of earthquakes?

Earthquakes are, therefore, largely confined to specific zones on the Earth, called **seismic zones**, and most of the rest of the surface of the Earth is relatively free from earthquakes. However, there are no areas of the Earth that are truly free of earthquakes.

ITQ 6 Most earthquake foci are less than 100 km below the surface, a few are between 100 and 700 km, and virtually none are deeper than this. Why do you think this is so?

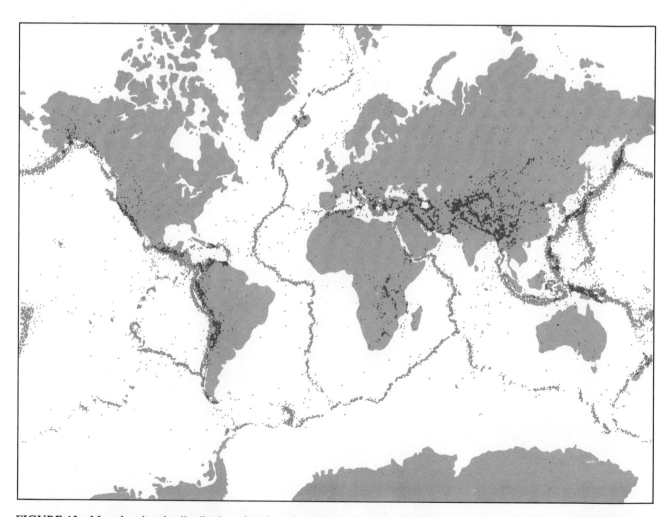

FIGURE 13   Map showing the distribution of earthquakes recorded between 1970 and 1983. Each small red dot represents a single epicentre.

1.7 HOW ARE EARTHQUAKES DETECTED AND RECORDED?

The science of earthquakes is known as **seismology**, from the Greek word *seismos*: 'a shaking'. When an earthquake, or seismic event, occurs a shock wave moves out from the focus and if it is a large earthquake the effects will be felt some distance from the epicentre (as, for example, the Mexico City event which was easily recorded in Britain). It is reported that, during a series of earthquakes with foci beneath the Mississippi Valley in 1811–1812, people sleeping in Washington DC (1 300 km away) were awakened, dishes rattled and walls cracked. The vibrations even set the church bells ringing in Boston, 1 700 km away. However, there comes a point when instrumental detection is the only reliable and objective method of detecting an earthquake. The instruments developed to detect earthquakes are called **seismometers**, devices that are so sensitive that they can detect and amplify even slight tremors of small earthquakes at great distances, and can record the movement automatically.

Seismometers (Figure 14) work on a simple principle: that a suspended heavy weight will remain stationary as the tremors pass, whereas the rest of the instrument that is in direct contact with the ground will vibrate. You should have no trouble in working out that the instrument in Figure 14a is designed to detect horizontal ground motions whereas that in Figure 14b records vertical motions.

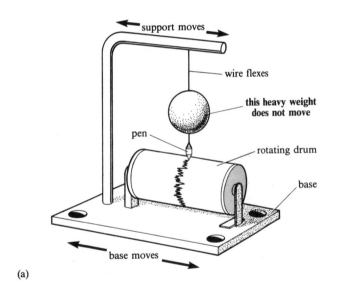

(a)

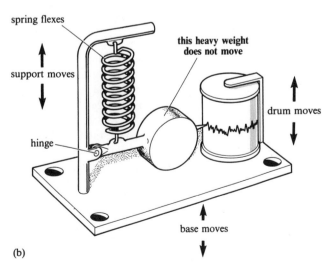

(b)

FIGURE 14   Two types of seismometer (see text for description): (a) detects horizontal ground motions (in the plane of the support and drum); (b) detects vertical ground motions.

☐ Can you think of any precautions that should be borne in mind when installing a set of seismometers?

■ They have to be isolated from any other sources of vibrations, such as heavy traffic, or underground trains.

Having set up our instruments, what would we record during an earthquake? The pen recorders would fluctuate up and down or from side to side to make a **seismic trace**, as shown diagrammatically on the drums in Figure 14. (The graph thus plotted is called a *seismogram*.)

How could you set up a system to record earthquakes? You know that earthquake shocks move out in all directions from the focus and, at the recording station, you want to know how 'big' the earthquake was and the direction from which it has come. As the vibration can arrive from any direction beneath your feet, you have a three-dimensional problem (Figure 15) and will need to use three instruments, each oriented differently, to make your recordings:

1   One instrument will be needed to record vertical (up and down) movements.

2   Two instruments will be needed to record horizontal movements:
(a) one aligned north–south
(b) one aligned east–west

This will allow the true amplitude and direction of the disturbance to be recorded.

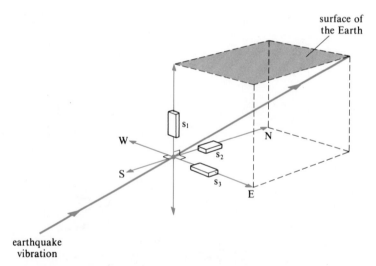

FIGURE 15   The true direction of motion of an earthquake vibration can be detected by three seismometers set up in directions at right angles to each other. S₁–S₃ are the three seismometers.

At Walton Hall we have sensitive instruments that work in very similar ways to seismometers but that also record minute changes in gravity. During the period 19–21 September 1985 when the Mexican earthquake and its aftershocks (defined below) occurred, a researcher found the trace shown in Figure 16 recorded on her instrument which was measuring the variation of 'tidal' acceleration due to the changing position of the Sun and Moon relative to the Earth. This is the regular sinusoidal recording on which are superimposed two large disturbances each lasting several hours and separated by about 36 hours. These disturbances are due entirely to the effects of tiny ground vibrations transmitted through the Earth from Mexico. The reason that there are two main disturbances shown on Figure 16 is that major earthquakes are rarely isolated events. Frequently, when a fault starts to move, there are several smaller earthquakes, sometimes before the main shock, called **foreshocks**, and sometimes following the main event,

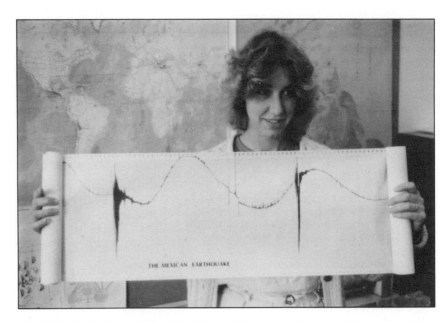

FIGURE 16   Seismic trace of the Mexico City earthquake, 19–21 September 1985, recorded at Walton Hall. For an explanation of the sinusoidal part of the recording, see the text. The main event (left) was recorded at 3.20 p.m. (UK time) on 19 September; the second large signal (towards the right) was recorded at 3.00 a.m. on 21 September and is the record of an aftershock.

called **aftershocks**. In the case of the Mexico City earthquake, the aftershocks, like that at 3 a.m. on 21 September (UK time), were particularly violent and caused many of the remaining buildings, damaged by the main event, finally to collapse.

Clearly, because its vibrations continue for a shorter time than those of the main earthquake, the aftershock shown in Figure 16 carried slightly less energy than the main event of 19 September; in other words it had a smaller magnitude. The **magnitude of an earthquake** is a measure of the maximum amount of ground motion caused by an earthquake, as recorded using a standard calibrated seismometer; it is therefore directly related to the amount of energy involved. The scale generally used is that developed by Charles Richter, working in California during the 1930s, and is called the **Richter scale**. Notice that it differs from Mercalli's intensity scale (based on descriptions of destructive effects) because it uses *instrumental* observations of the amount of ground motion caused by an earthquake. Richter and his colleagues devised the scale to give some way of differentiating 'small, medium and big earthquakes' that did not depend on factors such as building construction or underlying geology. It was intended to classify only local Californian earthquakes but is now the scale most frequently quoted to classify all earthquakes.

The magnitude of an earthquake cannot be read directly from the seismic trace as various corrections have to be made and, more importantly, the scale is **logarithmic**, which means that an increase of one unit on the magnitude scale implies an increase by a factor of 10 in the amount of the ground motion.

ITQ 7   What increase in the maximum amount of ground motion is involved in going from an earthquake that measures 5.5 on the Richter scale to one that registers 8.5?

TABLE 2 Comparative features describing the size of earthquakes

Magnitude	Approximate maximum intensity	Number per year	Equivalent destructive power
0	I	⎫	
1		⎬ 700 000	0.5 kg TNT
2		⎭	
2–2.9		300 000	
3	⎬ minor		
3–3.9		49 000	
4			
4–4.9		6 200	
5	VI		small atom bomb, 20 000 tonnes TNT (20 kilotonnes)
5–5.9	⎬ damaging	800	
6	VIII		hydrogen bomb, 1 000 000 tonnes TNT (1 megatonne)
6–6.9	⎬ destructive	120	
7	X		
7–7.9	major	18	
8	or		
8–8.9	XII ⎬ great	1 every few years	60 000 1-megatonne bombs

The Richter scale of magnitude is shown in Table 2, which also shows the Mercalli scale of intensity, and the destructive power in terms of the equivalent quantity of explosives or number of bombs. By measuring the earthquake effects of nuclear tests of known size, seismologists can calculate the energy release of earthquakes and monitor the size of other nuclear tests. We shall be returning to this topic towards the end of this double Unit.

☐ Earthquakes with high values on the Richter scale are not always the most devastating, nor do they cause the greatest loss of life. Why do you think this is so?

■ Devastation and loss of life depend on *where* the earthquake occurs; quite a small event can kill thousands in a densely populated area, but a higher magnitude earthquake may cause few deaths in a sparsely populated area.

Earthquakes that register 8 or more on the Richter scale ('major' or 'great' earthquakes) happen about once in every 10–20 years. Tables 3a and 3b show a selection of some of the largest, most devastating and famous earthquakes, both on a world scale and for Britain.

We have evidence that the effects of the earthquake that devastated Mexico City in 1985 travelled to Milton Keynes; in fact, the same earthquake could have been recorded with seismometers anywhere else on the Earth's surface. In the next Section you will learn about the speed and mode of travel of earthquake shocks as they move through the Earth.

We shall address such questions as:

What happens to the rocks when earthquake shocks pass through them?

What can we learn from the travel times of earthquake vibrations?

How can the spherical avocado pear model of the Earth be tested and modified experimentally?

TABLE 3a   Some important destructive earthquakes

Year	Date	Magnitude	Location	Estimated fatalities
856			Greece, Corinth	45 000
1268			Asia Minor: Silicia	60 000
1290			China: Chihli	100 000
1456			Italy: Naples	60 000
1531			Portugal: Lisbon	30 000
1556	23 Jan		China: Shansi	830 000
1667			Caucasia: Shemaka	60 000
1730	30 Dec		Japan: Hokkaido	137 000
1731			China: Peking	100 000
1737			India: Calcutta	300 000
1751			Morocco: Agadir	unknown
1755	1 Nov	8.75	Portugal: Lisbon	60 000
1835	20 Feb	8.5	Chile	35 (known)
1857	16 Dec	6.5	Italy	12 000
1868	13 Aug		Peru–Ecuador	40 000
1896	15 June		Japan: Riku-Ugo	27 120
1905	4 Apr	8.6	India: Kangra	19 000
1906	31 Jan	8.9	Colombia	1 000
	18 Apr	8.3	California: San Francisco	700
	17 Aug	8.6	Chile: Valparaiso	20 000
1908	28 Dec	7.5	Italy: Messina, Reggio	83 000
1915	13 Jan	7.0	Italy: Avezzano	29 980
1920	16 Dec	8.6	China: Kansu, Shansi	100 000
1923	1 Sept	8.3	Japan: Tokyo, Yokohama	143 000
1927	7 Mar	7.9	Japan: Tango	3 020
	22 May	8.3	China: Nan-Shan	200 000
1929	1 May	7.1	Iran: Shirwan	3 300
1931	2 Feb	7.9	New Zealand: Hawke's Bay	255
1933	2 Mar	8.9	Japan: Morioka	2 990
1934	15 Jan	8.4	India: Bihar–Nepal	10 700
1935	30 May	7.5	Pakistan: Quetta	30 000
1939	25 Jan	8.3	Chile: Talca	28 000
	26 Dec	7.9	Turkey: Erzincan	30 000
1944	7 Dec	8.3	Japan: Tonankai, Nankaido	1 000
1950	15 Aug	8.7	India, Assam, Tibet	1 530
1952	4 Mar	8.6	Japan: Tokachi	28
1955	31 Mar	7.9	Philippines: Mindanao	430
1956	9 June	7.7	Afghanistan: Kabul	220
1957	28 July	7.8	Mexico: Acapulco	55
1960	29 Feb	5.8	Morocco: Agadir	14 000
1962	1 Sept	7.3	Iran: Qazvin	12 230
1964	28 Mar	8.5	Alaska: Anchorage, Seward	178
1970	31 May	7.8	Peru: near Lima	66 000
1972	23 Dec	6.2	Nicaragua: Managua	5 000
1975	4 Feb	7.5	China: Haicheng	few
1976	4 Feb	7.9	Guatemala	22 000
	27 July	7.6	China: Tangshan	>250 000
1977	19 Aug	7.7	Indonesia	190
1980	23 Nov	7.0	Italy: Naples area	2 800
1983	26 May	7.7	Japan	101
1985	3 Mar	7.8	Chile	177
	24 Aug	7.4	China	60
	19 Sept	7.8	Mexico	>2 000
1987	2 Mar	6.5	New Zealand	few

TABLE 3b   Some British earthquakes

Year	Date	Magnitude	Location
1852	9 Nov		north Wales
1863	6 Oct		Hereford (Charles Dickens' letter)
1880	28 Nov		Oban
1896	17 Dec		Hereford
1906	27 Jun	5.2	Swansea
1926	15 Aug	4.8	Herefordshire
1931	1 June	5.5	Dogger Bank
1944	30 Dec	4.8	Skipton, north Yorkshire
1957	11 Feb	5.3	Derby
1979	26 Dec	4.8	Carlisle, Cumbria
1984	19 July	5.4	Lleyn Peninsula, Wales
1986	18 Nov	5.4	north Wales

You may recall reports of an earthquake in Colchester in 1884. This earthquake had a high intensity but a low magnitude.

21

SUMMARY OF SECTION I

1   The Earth has the shape of a slightly flattened sphere. It has a thin outer skin called the crust; below this is a thick layer called the mantle, then a central core.

2   Crustal rocks show a great variety of textures, representing different modes of formation, some as sedimentary rocks that were deposited at the Earth's surface and others as crystalline igneous rocks that cooled from a molten magma.

3   The density of crustal rocks is less than that of the mantle, or of the Earth as a whole. The density of rocks increases towards the centre of the Earth for various reasons, principally because of the increasingly high pressures. Temperatures also increase with depth inside the Earth but not at the same rate everywhere.

4   Earthquakes occur when rocks move along fractures, called faults. The point of origin of an earthquake is called its focus, and the point directly above this, on the Earth's surface, is called the epicentre.

5   Most earthquakes occur in seismic zones, for example the Circum-Pacific Belt and the Alpine–Himalayan Belt.

6   Earthquakes are detected and measured using seismometers, which record a seismic trace on a seismogram. Intensity is an observational measure of the damage caused by an earthquake and depends on local factors (Mercalli scale). Magnitude is an objective physical measure of the size of an earthquake and is measured on the Richter scale; 'major' or 'great' earthquakes register more than 8 on this scale.

SAQ I   Which of statements (a)–(d) are true and which are untrue about (i) the Mercalli scale and (ii) the Richter scale:

(a) It measures the magnitude of an earthquake. No Yes.

(b) It measures the intensity of an earthquake. Yes. Yes

(c) It has a maximum value of ten. No No

(d) It is a measure of the maximum amount of ground movement. No .No.

SAQ 2   Examine the damaged fences in Figure 17a and b. In terms of the types of faulting shown in Figure 11, what types of fault motion seem to have been acting on these fences?

FIGURE 17a and b   Photographs of earthquake damage to fences (for use with SAQ 2).

(a)

(b)

SAQ 3 *Without referring to Table 1*, complete the following Table to describe the characteristics of the rock hand specimens S1, S3, S4 and S6.

Specimen	Interlocking crystals?	Rounded grains?	Size of crystals or grains	Igneous or sedimentary
S1 granite	yes, 3 different minerals present	no	large, up to 4–5 mm	igneous
S3 basalt				
S4 peridotite				
S6 sandstone				

SAQ 4 Define (a) the focus of an earthquake and (b) the epicentre of an earthquake.

SAQ 5 Which of the following statements about earthquakes are true?

(a) The probability of an area experiencing a 'major' or 'great' earthquake is the same all over the world.

(b) Earthquakes can never happen in the same place twice.

(c) Earthquakes can happen under the oceans.

2 EARTHQUAKE WAVES: WHAT ARE THEY AND HOW DO THEY TRAVEL?

Towards the end of Section 1, we started using terms like 'earthquake vibrations' and 'shock waves' without being very specific about what we mean by *waves* and *vibrations* or about why earthquake waves radiate out in all directions from the focus of an earthquake. So what do we mean by 'waves'? This Section deals with the properties of waves and introduces the way in which earthquake waves are used to provide information about the materials through which they are transmitted.

2.1 WAVE MOTION: A LOOK AT WATER WAVES

You are probably familiar with various types of waves that occur on the surface of water. The type we are most interested in is the circular ripple-like motion that occurs when you drop a stone into a calm pond. We want to know what is *actually moving* across the surface of the pond.

You might like to try a simple experiment in a large sink or in the bath. All you need is a pencil and a small piece of cork or a similarly buoyant material. You will see more if you look across the water surface towards bright daylight (i.e. with a window behind the sink, as in Figure 18). With the tip of the pencil, touch the water surface, and keep on touching the same spot regularly at about one second intervals. Something travels across the *surface* of the water. But what is it that travels? Is it water itself? If the water travels, it will carry the cork with it, so drop the cork in the water about 10 cm away from the centre and repeat the experiment. You should see that the cork bobs up and down but does not move outwards. It is merely the *disturbance* caused by the pencil that travels out across the surface: there is no difference in the water surface before and after the wave

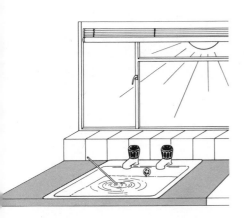

FIGURE 18   Generating water waves in a sink.

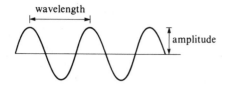

FIGURE 19 Two quantities used to characterize wave motion are the wavelength and the amplitude.

has passed. You will see shortly that the same kind of process occurs in solids, like the rock materials of which the Earth is made. The transmission of a disturbance in this way is called *wave propagation*. It follows that a wave is a simple, regularly repeating motion of a medium (see Figure 19). The distance between two successive identical points on the wave pattern measured in the direction of propagation is known as the **wavelength** and the maximum displacement of the wave from the average level is known as the **amplitude**.

2.2 SIMPLE SEISMIC WAVES

As with water waves, we must consider what it is that travels from the focus of an earthquake to the seismometer. First try this short exercise which will help to illustrate what follows.

ITQ 8 A seismometer of the type shown in Figure 14b measures the vertical displacement of the ground during the arrival of the disturbance due to vibrations from a distant earthquake. A very precise internal clock is used to record time in milliseconds ($1\,\mathrm{ms} = 10^{-3}\,\mathrm{s}$). Table 4 gives the displacements recorded over the first 300 ms. Plot these displacement values against time using the grid in Figure 20. We have plotted the first four values to give you a start.

TABLE 4 Vertical displacement of the ground as a function of time for a distant earthquake

Time/ms	5	20	30	40	55	70	85	100	120	135
Displacement/mm	0.15	0.65	0.85	0.98	0.94	0.67	0.17	−0.34	−0.87	−1.00
Time/ms	145	155	170	185	200	220	230	240	260	275
Displacement/mm	−0.94	−0.77	−0.34	0.17	0.64	0.97	0.98	0.86	0.34	−0.17

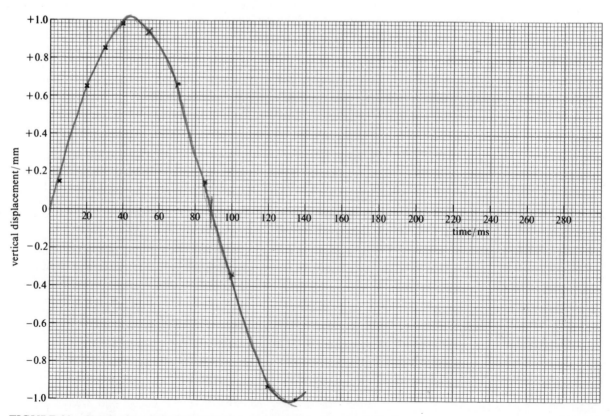

FIGURE 20 Graph of vertical displacement against time (for use with ITQ 8).

WAVELENGTH

AMPLITUDE OF A WAVE

SEISMIC ENERGY

ELASTICITY

When you have plotted these points, try to draw a smooth curve connecting them.

(a) Is the graph a smooth curve? *Yes*.

(b) Does the displacement vary in a systematic way? *Yes*.

(c) What is the period of the disturbance, i.e. how long does it take before the disturbance repeats itself so that one wavelength passes? *about 180 ms*.

Thus, the ground displacement in the example of wave motion given in ITQ 8 repeats itself regularly with time, so is *periodic*. In this particular case, the period of the disturbance is 180 ms. Before we leave ITQ 8 you should note that the displacements you have plotted occur because energy, in this case **seismic energy**, has been transmitted through the ground from an earthquake. This is analogous to the energy you applied with the tip of a pencil to the water surface (Section 2.1). As in the water example, the seismic energy is dissipated gradually through the motion of the rocks and ground surface that it causes.

☐ What do you think will happen to the *amplitude* (i.e. the maximum displacement—1 mm in our example) of our seismic wave observations when the earthquake is over and no further energy is pushed into the ground?

■ Gradually, the amplitude will fall to zero, until the ground surface, just like the water surface in Figure 18, again becomes stationary.

You will be learning much more about energy in Unit 9.

2.3 TWO TYPES OF SEISMIC WAVE

So far we have thought of seismic waves as causing displacements of the ground, both vertically (as in ITQ 8) and horizontally, due to the transmission of seismic energy from an earthquake. The true direction of wave motion is given by the maximum amplitude of the disturbance in three dimensions, as shown in Figure 15. But to keep matters simple, we shall consider only the motions directly along paths from earthquake foci to receiving seismometers. What actually happens to the material along this particular path? To help you think this one out, imagine a row of balls, connected by springs and suspended by very fine threads (Figure 21). You should be able to do this experiment in your mind's eye—as a *thought experiment* (Unit 1). Before we start, it is worth commenting that the tiny individual components of which rocks are made—at the scale of *atoms* (Units 11–12) are equivalent to tiny balls connected together by 'springs' in three-dimensional arrays.

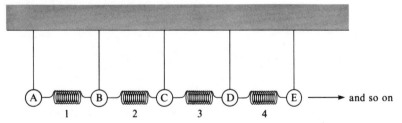

FIGURE 21   Ball-and-spring model for compressional wave propagation.

Suppose you were to give ball A in Figure 21 a sharp push to the right. What do you think would happen? As ball A moves towards ball B, it compresses spring 1. Springs have **elasticity**, by which we mean that after being distorted by the application of a force, they return to their original shape when the force is removed. So spring 1 does not stay compressed; it returns to its original length and thereby pushes ball B to the right and ball A to the left. Ball B, which in turn moves to the right and back again, squeezes spring 2 and transmits the same effect to ball C. This process continues down the line of balls and springs: in our model (Figure 21) this

COMPRESSION PULSE

RAREFACTION PULSE

COMPRESSIONAL WAVE MOTION

P-WAVES

TRANSVERSE WAVE MOTION

represents the travelling of a *pulse* due to the original compression of spring 1. This is known as a **compression pulse**, and as it travels down the line of balls and springs it leaves behind springs that are *temporarily* stretched to greater than their original length. This stretching is known as *rarefaction* or *dilatation* and it follows that each compression pulse is followed by a **rarefaction pulse**.

To make this more clear, look at Figure 22 which shows the same effect in a long block of rock, of square cross-section on which we have drawn a uniform square grid. Imagine that the left-hand face of the block is struck regularly with a hammer to generate compressional pulses that pass down the length of the block. One such pulse is marked by a black arrow and you can see that it moves progressively along the block (Figure 22b–f). In advance of and behind this compression pulse travel rarefaction pulses where the material is expanded relative to its undeformed state.

☐ Now concentrate on one tiny square on the side of the block—we have marked one in black to help you—and describe its change in shape and size during the time between successive pulses (i.e. one cycle).

■ The square expands to a larger rectangle, extended in the direction of motion, as a rarefaction pulse passes. It then returns through its original size to a smaller rectangle, compressed in the direction of motion, as a compression pulse passes, and finally expands to its original size (Figure 22f), to complete the cycle. Throughout, the shape is that of a rectangle, but the length, and hence area, of the rectangle changes continuously.

Can you see that you have just described one complete cycle of a type of wave motion? It does not matter when we start in the cycle (i.e. compression first or rarefaction first) so long as we describe all the stages involved before the pattern of motion repeats itself. Clearly, it is a type of wave motion and the similarity to the wave motions you plotted in ITQ 8 is quite striking, especially if you turn Figure 22 through 90° and think of the pulses coming up towards the Earth's surface!

Now go back to that small rectangle and think about what happens *in three dimensions*. You should be able to appreciate that the change in area of the original square on the side of the block represents a change in *volume* of the equivalent cube that exists behind the square face inside the block. This type of wave motion *in which there is a change in volume without a change in shape* (all angles within the affected volume stay at 90°) is known as **compressional wave motion**. As early as the 1800s theoretical physicists had convinced themselves that compressional waves should pass through elastic bodies, but it was not until the beginning of this century that seismologists had devised instruments sensitive enough to detect them in rocks. Compressional seismic waves are commonly known as **P-waves** partly because their motion is of the push–pull variety, and the disturbance consists of a pressure pulse. Originally they were called P-waves because they are the first, or *primary* waves to arrive at a seismometer after an earthquake (see later in this Section).

Notice in Figure 22 that, as with our water waves (Figure 18), the material returns to its original size after the wave has passed. In other words, the block of rock acts as a medium to carry the waves but does not become permanently deformed. Another significant feature of P-waves is that the *motion of the material takes place in the direction of propagation*. But there is another important kind of seismic wave where the motions are different.

☐ Going back to Figure 21, can you think of another way of displacing ball A which might cause a different kind of disturbance to travel down the line?

■ You could push ball A sideways, in a direction *perpendicular* to the line of springs.

In Figure 23 you are looking *down* on top of a line of balls and springs. You will appreciate that if ball A is displaced horizontally from side to side another type of pulse, a '*shake*' pulse, will travel down the line, and Figure

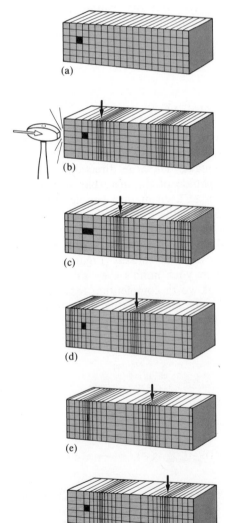

(a)

(b)

(c)

(d)

(e)

(f)

FIGURE 22 Stages (a–f) in the deformation of a block of material with the passage of compressional waves from left to right. The arrows indicate the progress of the first compression pulse along the block.

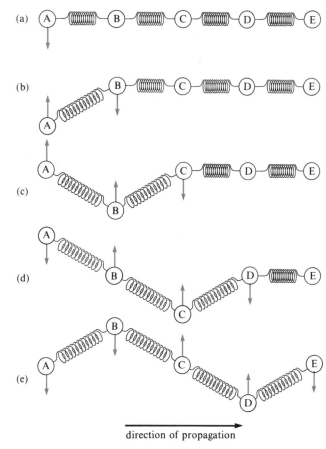

FIGURE 23 Sideways propagation of a disturbance down a line of balls and springs as in Figure 21. Here, you are looking *down* on top of the line, and ball A is moved from side to side. The stages (a–e) show the effect down the line of one complete 'cycle' of transverse movement of A. (The red arrows indicate the directions of the forces acting on the balls during the cycle.)

23 shows the progress of the pulse at five successive instants. In Figure 23e, the first sideways movement of ball A is about to affect ball E as a new shake pulse begins at A. We call this **transverse wave motion** because the individual particles—balls in our model—are *vibrating at right angles to the direction of wave propagation* (note the contrast with compressional waves).

Now examine Figure 24 which illustrates the passage of transverse waves through a block of rock material.

☐ Here we have shown a hammer hitting the block vertically, at right angles to the horizontal direction of wave propagation. The same effect would be achieved if the block were hit horizontally, on the front face, but still at right angles to the direction of wave propagation. What kind of fault motion do you think is required to set off transverse earthquake waves? Look back to Figure 11 if necessary.

■ The answer is *shearing* motion. You may have found this a bit tricky to answer, but look back to Figure 11c which shows horizontal fault movements at the ground surface. As the fault moves, by a sudden wrenching, the ground to either side is jerked with transverse motion.

Having looked at faults again, you probably realize that *all* faults, whether their motion is near vertical or horizontal, will generate transverse waves as they move. In that case, you might wonder how compressional waves are produced during faulting. The answer is that *both* types of seismic wave are generated every time a fault moves but, whereas most of the transverse wave energy is transmitted at right angles to the direction of faulting, most of the compressional wave energy is transmitted closer to the direction of motion (given by the black arrows in Figure 11). In most directions, however, you can take it that there is a combination of both compressional and transverse wave motions.

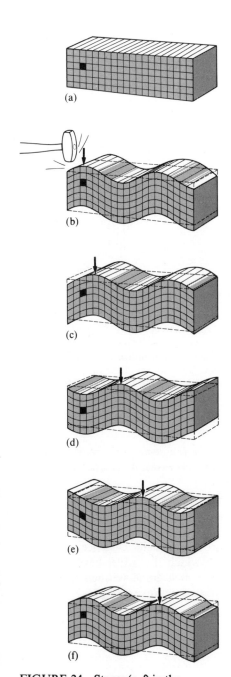

FIGURE 24 Stages (a–f) in the deformation of a block with the passage of transverse waves from left to right. The arrows indicate the position of maximum displacement during the passage of one cycle of deformation along the block.

27

S-WAVES

STRESS

STRAIN

ELASTIC MODULUS

ITQ 9 Returning to Figure 24, concentrate on the effect of transverse waves on the square grid along the side of the block; in particular follow the changes taking place in the small black square from Figure 24a to f.

(a) Summarize the changes in the shape of the original square and thus in the volume of material behind the black front face.

(b) How do these changes differ from those associated with P-waves?

Transverse seismic waves, produced by shearing motions, are commonly known as **S-waves**, partly because their motion is produced by *shaking*, but originally because they are the *secondary* waves to arrive at a seismometer. This is shown in Figure 25: the first waves to arrive are simple compressional P-waves, followed some time later (typically, several minutes later) by S-waves and even later still by a third kind of seismic wave, known as *L-waves*. In fact L-waves (or Love waves after the man who first described them) travel around the surface of the Earth, whereas P- and S-waves travel *through* the Earth and the greater distance travelled goes some way to explaining why L-waves arrive last. Since we are interested in the Earth's interior, we shall be dealing only with P- and S-waves.

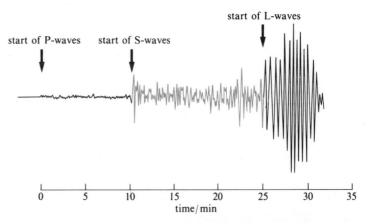

FIGURE 25   Seismogram of an earthquake with epicentre at Erzincan, Turkey, recorded at Cambridge, Massachusetts, USA, on 26 December 1939. The first arrivals (left) are small deflections made by P-waves alone; then come large deflections made mainly by S-waves, with a small P contribution; and finally there are even larger deflections mainly from L-waves, but with small P and S contributions. The time that elapsed between the start of the P-waves and the start of the S-waves indicates that the distance from the epicentre to the recording station is about 77° or 8 560 km.

☐ Given that P- and S-waves travel *along the same path* from source to receiver, and that P-waves arrive before S-waves, what does this imply about the relative speeds of the waves?

■ S-waves travel more slowly than P-waves: S-waves take longer than P-waves to complete the same journey.

Now the speed of wave propagation provides crucial evidence about the physical properties of the media through which the waves have travelled. That is one of the main reasons why we have gone to such trouble to distinguish between the two main types of seismic wave motion.

2.4 WAVE SPEEDS—WHAT DO THEY DEPEND ON?

For simplicity, we will start by considering P-waves. Think again about the row of balls and springs shown in Figure 21.

ITQ 10 Would the compression pulse travel faster or slower down the line of balls and springs if:

(a) the same initial force were applied to a row of balls with a greater mass, but with the springs unchanged;

(b) the springs were stiffer (i.e. less compressible, so more force would be needed to compress or stretch them by a given amount), but the balls were unchanged and were displaced by the same amount?

(Hint: Think of changes in the motion of the balls in terms of Newton's second law, $F = ma$—Unit 3.)

In the answer to ITQ 10a we have concluded that increasing the mass of a fixed volume will cause P-waves to be transmitted more slowly. Since greater mass in the same volume means a greater *density* we can say that:

As density increases, P-wave speed decreases

Next we need to develop a similar statement relating P-wave speeds to compressibility using the arguments in ITQ 10b. First you need to know that, although rocks are much less compressible than springs, each rock has a characteristic 'stiffness'. This characteristic property of any material (rock or otherwise) can be defined in terms of the ratio of the force that is applied to a unit area of the rock (**stress**) to the 'distortion' (**strain**) that results. This ratio is called the **elastic modulus** and it is defined as follows:

$$\text{elastic modulus} = \frac{\text{stress}}{\text{strain}} \tag{3}$$

We will now examine the terms in Equation 3 more rigorously. In the case of a P-wave travelling through a solid, the forces are compressional, so we have compressional stress. For P-waves, stress is the same physical quantity as pressure, which we defined in Section 1.3.1 as the perpendicular force acting on a unit area (Equation 1). To make this clear, imagine a slice of rock cut at right angles to the direction of wave propagation (Figure 26),

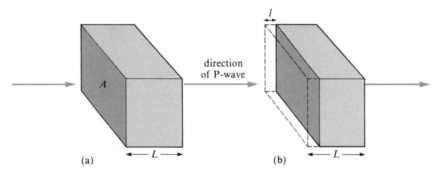

FIGURE 26 The effect of a compressional pulse acting on a slab of material, of length L and cross-sectional area A: (a) before deformation; (b) after deformation has shortened the length by l.

rather like a slimmed-down version of one of our cubes in Figure 22. Imagine also that the slice is constrained so that it cannot expand sideways as a result of the compression. If the cross-sectional area of the slice is A and if the compressional force acting on the slice is F, then:

$$\text{stress} = F/A \tag{4}$$

(In SI units, stress, like pressure, is measured in $N\,m^{-2}$.)

If the original length of the slice in the direction of propagation is L, and a compression pulse, due to the applied stress, reduces this length by l (Figure 26b), then the degree of deformation is the change in length l divided by the original length L. This is called the *strain*.

$$\text{strain} = l/L \tag{5}$$

Notice that strain has no units—it is a length divided by a length so it is simply a number. Notice also that the definitions of stress and strain apply equally to an extensional stress producing an increase in length, as occurs during passage of a rarefaction pulse. If you have any difficulty remembering which is stress and which is strain, just bear in mind that, as in life, *strain* is the result of *stress*!

Now we are in a position to go back to the description of stiffness that we introduced in Equation 3. The elastic modulus that tells us how rock will behave under compression when it is prevented from expanding or contracting sideways—the normal situation deep in the Earth—is called the **axial modulus**, and it is represented by the Greek letter ψ ('psi'). Using Equation 3 for the case of compression:

$$\text{axial modulus} = \frac{\text{compressional stress}}{\text{compressional strain}}$$

$$\text{or} \qquad \psi = \frac{F/A}{l/L} \tag{6}$$

Note that axial modulus has the same SI units (N m^{-2}) as stress or pressure, since strain is a dimensionless quantity. It follows that the greater the value of axial modulus, the greater the stress required to cause a given strain. In other words, the axial modulus is really a measure of the *incompressibility* of the medium: the higher its numerical value, the less easily will the medium be compressed. Now, in the answer to ITQ 10b we deduced that waves travel faster in a stiffer, less compressible medium, so we can conclude:

As axial modulus increases, P-wave speed increases

The two relationships we have just derived:

P-wave speed increases as density decreases

P-wave speed increases as axial modulus increases

do not quite tell the whole story. When P-waves travel through layers of different materials with different values of density and axial modulus, they also change *direction*. For this reason, Earth scientists commonly use the term *velocity* when discussing the propagation of seismic waves. (You will recall from Unit 3 that speed is just the *magnitude* of velocity, and takes no account of direction.)

We are now going to develop a quantitative relationship between density, elastic modulus and the speed of seismic waves, by taking two steps:

(i) First we shall derive expressions for the speeds, or *magnitudes of the velocities*, of P-waves and S-waves. We shall use the symbols v_P and v_S, but remember that, strictly, these are not velocities, just speeds.

(ii) Next we shall consider how changes in speeds v_P and v_S become changes in *velocities* when the waves change their *directions* of propagation at the boundaries between different materials which have different densities and elastic moduli.

Taking stock, we now know that the magnitude of the velocity (i.e. speed) of P-waves (v_P) and rock density (ρ) are related as follows:

v_P increases as ρ decreases

which is the same as saying

v_P increases as $1/\rho$ increases $\tag{7}$

The other important fact we know is that:

$$v_P \text{ increases as } \psi \text{ increases} \qquad (8)$$

ITQ 11 Looking at Equations 7 and 8 you might expect that the relationship between v_P, ρ and ψ would be:

$$v_P \propto \psi/\rho$$

(a) Work out the dimensions of ψ/ρ and determine whether these are the dimensions of speed.

(b) Can you suggest a better relationship between these three quantities?

It follows from the reasoning in ITQ 11 that $v_P \propto \sqrt{\psi/\rho}$; in fact, the equation that relates v_P, ρ and ψ is:

$$v_P = \sqrt{\psi/\rho} \qquad (9)$$

Putting this equation into words, the speed of P-waves in any material is equal to the square root of the material's axial modulus divided by its density. Equation 9 is an extremely important relationship which we shall be using throughout the rest of our discussion of seismic waves. Clearly, if we can measure the magnitude of the velocity of P-waves in certain parts of the Earth's interior then we can say something about the values of axial modulus and density. As you will see, this in turn can tell us about the possible materials of which the Earth is made. To get a feel for how Equation 9 works, try ITQ 12.

ITQ 12 (a) For a fixed density, what happens to the speed of P-waves v_P as axial modulus increases by factors of 2, 3 and 4?

(b) For a fixed axial modulus, what happens to v_P if density increases by the same factors?

We shall give you some actual numbers for axial modulus and density to try out in a moment, but first we must consider S-waves. The reasoning that we have used in leading up to Equation 9 can be repeated for S-waves, except that instead of the axial modulus (which has to do with compressional stress), we should use an elastic modulus which relates to the stress accompanying the transverse motion by which S-waves are transmitted. This kind of stress is called **shear stress** and the deformation which it produces is called **shear strain**. For the purposes of our discussion, however, we do not need to go into the detailed definitions of shear stress and shear strain. The ratio of stress to strain is, as before, an elastic modulus. In the case of S-waves, it is called the **rigidity modulus**, which has the symbol μ (the Greek letter 'mu'), and it is given by the relationship:

$$\text{rigidity modulus } \mu = \frac{\text{shear stress}}{\text{shear strain}} \qquad (10)$$

Whereas the axial modulus gives the ability of a medium to resist compressional stresses that cause changes in volume rather than shape (Figure 22) the rigidity modulus is a measure of its ability to resist *shear deformations* that cause changes of *shape* rather than *volume* (Figure 24). If for S-wave speeds we now apply a similar type of reasoning to that which led to Equation 9 for P-waves, it follows that:

$$v_S = \sqrt{\mu/\rho} \qquad (11)$$

A typical rock has an axial modulus ψ of $3 \times 10^{11} \, \text{N m}^{-2}$ whereas its rigidity modulus μ is about $8 \times 10^{10} \, \text{N m}^{-2}$. Indeed, rigidity moduli for most solids are less than their axial moduli.

SEISMIC REFRACTION

NORMAL

ANGLE OF INCIDENCE

ANGLE OF REFRACTION

SNELL'S LAW

$$\rho = 5.5 \times 10^3$$
$$\psi = 3 \times 10^{11}$$
$$\mu = 8 \times 10^{10}$$
$$V_p = \sqrt{\psi/\rho} = \sqrt{\dfrac{3 \times 10^{11}}{5.5 \times 10^3}}$$
$$= 7385 \ m/s$$
$$= 7.38 \ km/s$$

☐ What do these values imply about the abilities of rocks to resist compressional and shear deformation?

■ Axial modulus is larger than rigidity modulus for typical rocks so rocks resist compression more effectively than they resist shear.

In other words, so far as elastic deformation is concerned (i.e. the non-permanent deformation due to the passage of seismic waves) it is easier to bend rocks than to compress them. The same is true of the springs that connect the balls in the models we discussed earlier.

☐ Can you predict from this information whether P-waves will travel faster or slower than S-waves?

■ Since ψ is greater than μ, P-waves will travel faster than S-waves in the same medium (as, indeed, we concluded from Figure 25).

ITQ 13 Now use the values for axial and rigidity moduli given on p. 31 for a typical rock, together with the average density for Earth materials ($5.5 \times 10^3 \ \mathrm{kg \, m^{-3}}$), to calculate, in units of $\mathrm{km \, s^{-1}}$, the speeds of P-waves and S-waves in these materials.

You may have been surprised at just how fast earthquake waves travel through Earth materials. Now another important question: Can both P-waves and S-waves be transmitted through a liquid? Liquids are normally quite difficult to compress and so they transmit P-waves. But the rigidity modulus of liquids is extremely small and for our purposes can be taken as zero. Now a substance with a zero rigidity modulus cannot be bent, and will have a v_S value of zero (Equation 11). As you will see in Section 4, this difference in the seismic properties of liquids is an important clue to the nature of the materials through which seismic waves pass in parts of the Earth's interior.

There is one more important aspect of their characteristics that you need to know, however, and that concerns the behaviour of seismic waves as they pass from layer to layer where the propagation velocities are different.

2.5 REFRACTION AND REFLECTION OF SEISMIC WAVES

So far, we have considered only seismic waves travelling through rocks of uniform elastic modulus and density. Clearly, the real Earth is a lot more complicated. For example, you know from Section 1.3.3 that density increases with depth in the Earth. The values of elastic moduli are also likely to increase because the extremely high pressures deep inside the Earth will squash the materials and make them less compressible (more incompressible) and more rigid. In fact, for a given rock type, the values of axial and rigidity moduli usually increase *faster* than density with increasing compression.

☐ Would you expect P-wave and S-wave speeds to increase or decrease with depth in a layer made of one rock type?

■ If elastic moduli increase more rapidly than density with increasing depth then both speeds should increase with depth. (Refer back to Equations 9 and 11 if you had trouble answering this and note that the top of each expression inside the square root sign is increasing faster than the bottom.) We shall come back to this in Section 4.

Of course, even the most casual observation of the rocks making up, say, the cliffs around the British coastline will reveal contrasts in rock type. For example, the cliffs of Dover are made from a relatively soft white limestone which is fundamentally different from the granite rocks of Land's End or the hard sandstone of north-east Scotland.

□ If two different rock types like these were found in contact (as happens in some places in Britain) do you think seismic wave speeds would remain unchanged in passing from one to the other?

■ This is most unlikely, as the elastic properties and densities of the two rock types are likely to be different. For the two speeds to be the same, the ratios ψ/ρ and μ/ρ would have to be the same for both rocks.

So seismic wave speeds are likely to vary between rock layers. But it is perhaps less obvious that the *direction* in which waves travel also changes as they cross the boundary from one type of rock to another. In other words, it is not just the speed but also the *velocity* that changes. This change of direction, as a seismic wave crosses from one rock type to another in which it has a different propagation velocity, is known as **seismic refraction** and it is a direct consequence of the wave nature of the disturbance. *All* wave-type disturbances are refracted in this way as they meet a boundary between two media with different speeds of propagation. (As you will see when you study Unit 10, light can be considered as a certain type of wave motion, and it too undergoes refraction when it enters a medium in which its speed is different.) Although we shall not discuss in any detail *how* the refraction occurs, as with the axial and rigidity moduli, it is possible to work out a theoretical description of what happens as the wave crosses the boundary, and this can be verified by experiment.

For simplicity, in the diagrams that follow we shall use straight lines to represent the paths of individual waves, be they P- or S-waves, passing through the Earth's layers. Remember that wave motion is more complex than this (Figures 22 and 24) and, moreover, that there are many wave paths from a single seismic source. Consider Figure 27, which shows the path of a seismic wave of speed v_1 entering a medium in which the speed is v_2. An imaginary line drawn at right angles to the boundary at the point at which the wave meets the boundary is called the **normal**, and the angle i between the normal and the incoming or *incident* wave path is called the **angle of incidence**. The corresponding angle r between the normal and the departing or *refracted* wave is called the **angle of refraction**. The relationship between these four quantities v_1, v_2, i and r is known as **Snell's law**.

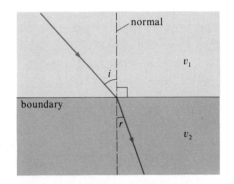

FIGURE 27 A wave undergoing refraction on passing through a boundary between two media in which the speeds of propagation (v_1 and v_2) are different; the angle of incidence is i and the angle of refraction is r.

$$\boxed{\begin{array}{l} \text{Snell's law} \\[4pt] \dfrac{\sin i}{\sin r} = \dfrac{v_1}{v_2} \end{array}} \tag{12}$$

In other words, the change in velocity is such that the ratio of the sine* of the angle of incidence to the sine of the angle of refraction is the same as the ratio of the *speeds* in the media where incidence and refraction take place.

ITQ 14   To give you some idea of how Equation 12 works try the following calculations. Assume that the angle of incidence i is 40° and calculate the angle of refraction r if:

(a) $v_2 = 1.5v_1$ (i.e. v_2 is greater than v_1 by 50%);

(b) $v_1 = 1.5v_2$ (i.e. v_1 is greater than v_2 by 50%).

(c) From your calculations in (a) and (b) state what happens *in general* to the direction followed by a wave when it passes from one medium to another in which its speed is different.

(d) What do you deduce about the relative values of v_1 and v_2 in Figure 27?

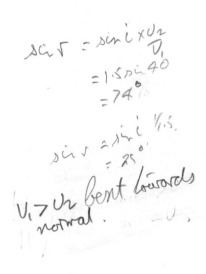

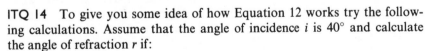

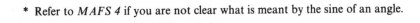

* Refer to *MAFS 4* if you are not clear what is meant by the sine of an angle.

ANGLE OF REFLECTION

CRITICAL ANGLE OF INCIDENCE

TOTAL REFLECTION

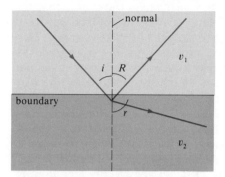

FIGURE 28 A wave meeting a boundary at which it is partially refracted and partially reflected.

The answer to ITQ 14 is very important; part (c) contains a crucial result which is a consequence of Snell's law:

> When a wave passes from a medium of *higher to lower* seismic wave speed, it will be refracted *towards* the normal, whereas when a wave passes from a medium of *lower to higher* seismic wave speed, it is refracted *away from* the normal.

So you can see that it is possible to work out from the sizes of the angles of incidence and refraction which of the two materials has the higher wave speed. Moreover, if we know the two angles and one speed, the second speed can be calculated. Conversely, knowing the ratio of wave speeds v_1/v_2, it is possible to work out the angle of refraction for any particular angle of incidence and vice versa.

Now look at Figure 28 which again shows an incident wave impinging on a v_1–v_2 boundary at an angle i. Here we show two subsequent wave paths, one within the second layer making an angle r with the normal which is the refracted wave, and a second which is reflected back into the first layer on the other side of the normal, at an angle R. This illustrates another general law of wave propagation:

> When a wave meets a boundary between two layers of different seismic wave speed, part of the energy of the wave is *refracted* and part is simultaneously *reflected*.

In this case, the **angle of reflection** R is equal to the angle of incidence i,

$$R = i \tag{13}$$

☐ Look at the sizes of the angles of incidence and refraction in Figure 28 and decide in which layer seismic wave speeds are greater.

■ Since i is less than r, $\sin i$ is less than $\sin r$, so $\sin i/\sin r$ will be less than 1. Hence, v_1/v_2 will be less than 1. Thus wave speed will be greater in the second (lower) layer—the opposite of the case in Figure 27.

The general statement above about the energy of a seismic wave being split into refracted and reflected components is true for all situations where refraction *can* take place—in fact most of the energy in a case like Figure 28 is transmitted to the refracted wave. But what happens if we *increase the angle of incidence* in a situation where the wave enters a layer of higher wave speed? Look at Figures 29–31 which show what happens to the incident wave for three different angles of incidence. In Figure 29 most of the energy is refracted at an angle r which is greater than i. As the angle of

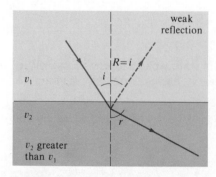

FIGURE 29 A wave undergoing refraction on passing into a medium of higher speed of propagation.

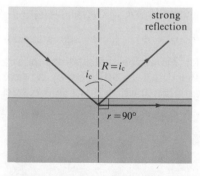

FIGURE 30 As the angle of incidence increases a point is reached at which the angle of refraction is 90° and most of the energy of the wave is reflected.

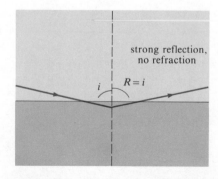

FIGURE 31 At much larger angles of incidence, there is no refraction, only reflection.

incidence increases, the angle of refraction also increases until at a certain value of i the value of r reaches 90° (Figure 30). At this point the refracted wave travels close to the boundary, just inside the material with the higher wave speed, and is much reduced in energy. Meanwhile, the energy of the reflected wave has increased.

ITQ 15   To illustrate this effect, take the situation in ITQ 14a where $v_1/v_2 = 1/1.5$ and simply calculate the values of i for which $r = 90°$. (Hint: $\sin 90° = 1$.)

There is a refracted wave for all angles of incidence *smaller* than the value you have just calculated, but at higher values of i there is *no* refracted wave, so the wave is completely reflected (see Figure 31).

The situation shown in Figure 30 is a critical geometry for refraction and reflection. At *smaller* angles of incidence, most of the energy is refracted into the high-speed layer, and at *larger* angles of incidence there is strong reflection but no refraction. That is why the angle of incidence in this case is known as the **critical angle of incidence**, usually labelled i_c. You began to see in ITQ 15 how this situation is described by Snell's law. At the critical angle, the angle of refraction r is 90°, so that the value of $\sin r$ is 1, and from Snell's Law:

$$\sin i_c = \frac{v_1}{v_2} \tag{14}$$

In words, the sine of the critical angle is the ratio of the wave speeds (with the smaller value on the top of the fraction, since the sine of an angle can never be greater than 1).

So we have seen that when a seismic wave meets a seismic boundary across which the wave speed increases, there is a value of the angle of incidence above which the wave energy is totally reflected. **Total reflection** cannot happen at a boundary across which the wave speed *decreases*, however, since the angle of refraction r is always *smaller* than the angle of incidence (Figure 27; Equation 12). Thus refraction is possible even at angles of incidence approaching 90°.

We need to consider the principles of refraction and reflection, and the phenomenon of the critical angle of incidence, in just a little more detail before we can apply them to the investigation of the Earth's interior. At the beginning of this Section we told you that seismic wave speeds *increase* with depth in a layer composed of one rock type. This means that, because of refraction, the velocities of the waves also change, so they cannot travel in straight lines. Imagine that such a layer is made up of a whole series of sub-layers, each of higher wave speed than the one above. At each sub-layer boundary, the waves will be refracted more and more *away* from the normal at the point of incidence (Figure 29), following a path from A to B in Figure 32.

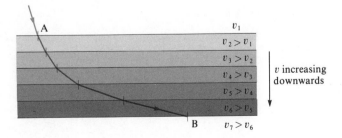

FIGURE 32   Wave refraction across boundaries between layers with speed increasing downwards layer by layer.

☐   What do you think will happen when a sub-layer boundary is reached at which the wave arrives at the critical angle of incidence (i.e. at point B)?

■   The refracted wave will travel parallel to the boundary within the lower layer (as in Figure 30).

CONTINUOUS REFRACTION

But wait a minute—Figure 32 shows horizontal parallel layers whereas the Earth is *curved*. Because of the Earth's curvature (upwards, towards the downwards propagating wave) such a wave must immediately re-enter the lower-speed layer above as a *reflected* wave.

☐ Suppose the wave is reflected at B in Figure 32, what will happen then?

■ It will then begin to follow a path back to the surface of identical shape to that followed on the way down, with refraction towards the normal at each boundary, because it is travelling upwards through sub-layers of decreasing seismic wave speed.

This situation is shown in Figure 33a; eventually the seismic wave returns to the surface at C where it may be detected by a seismometer.

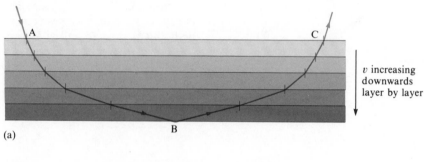

(a)

FIGURE 33   Wave refraction (a) across very thin layers with speed increasing with depth, and (b) through rock with seismic speed continuously increasing with depth. (*Note:*   In the real Earth the layers curve slightly upwards and this favours a curved wave path of the type shown here.)

(b)

We have been considering the effects of refraction in a series of sub-layers, but within many of the Earth's layers there is an almost continuous increase of seismic speed with depth. If you can think of this continuous increase as occurring across a very large number of very thin layers, each of which has a very slightly higher seismic speed than the one above, then you should be able to see that the wave follows a path that is very close to a smooth curve. This situation is shown in Figure 33b where the wave curves down from the surface, and then back to the surface again. This effect is called **continuous refraction**, and it is an important feature of the behaviour of seismic waves travelling through the Earth's interior. Continuous refraction will occur for an infinite number of wave paths all radiating out from the source. Although we have shown only one wave in Figure 33b, there are innumerable others, all curved, as shown in Figure 34. Each of them

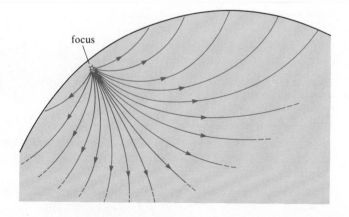

FIGURE 34   Seismic waves are radiated in all possible directions after an earthquake; each wave path is curved if speed increases with depth (as shown in Figure 33).

reaches a maximum depth of penetration *half-way between the source and the detecting seismometer* but, of course, for any seismic disturbance only one wave is detected in this illustration for each seismometer position.

The final feature of seismic wave propagation we need to consider is observed when a layer with lower seismic speed is sandwiched between two other layers with higher speed (Figure 35). If an earthquake occurs within the low-speed layer and radiates waves in all directions, those that travel along paths such as 1, 2 or 3 can pass out of the lower-speed layer, being refracted away from the normal as they do so. Along path 4, however, the angle of incidence is the critical angle i_c so that the wave is reflected back into the low-speed layer. It then passes across this layer and strikes the opposite boundary, again at the critical angle, and is reflected once more. The wave is thus *trapped* within the layer that has a lower seismic wave speed than the layers above and below.

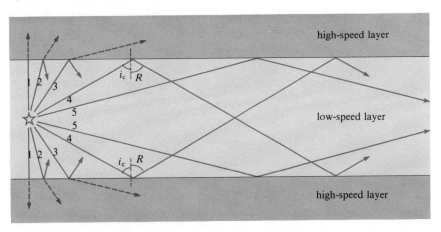

FIGURE 35 The trapping of waves in a low-speed layer.

2.6 EARTHQUAKES—SEISMOLOGY AT WORK (TV PROGRAMME)

This programme illustrates many of the more important concepts that you have met so far in this double Unit; it concentrates on various aspects of earthquakes and recording devices (seismometers) and looks at the interpretation of seismic wave travel times in terms of the broad structural subdivisions of the Earth.

Starting with some dramatic film of the 1964 Alaskan earthquake we visit an earthquake simulation table at the University of Bristol in order to study the effects of earthquakes in terms of Mercalli's intensity scale (Table 2, Section 1.7). A revision of the two main types of seismic wave motion (based on animated versions of Figures 22 and 24) is followed by an examination of various types of seismometer design, both ancient and modern (Plates 21a and 21b). Next we visit an underground bunker at the Blacknest Observatory (Newbury, Berkshire) where the use of some modern electronic seismometers is described by Peter Marshall. The important feature to note is that the relative movement between a heavy magnet and a surrounding electrical coil is used to create an electrical signal during a seismic event. The heavy magnet remains stationary while the body of the instrument (including the coil) vibrates with the ground. The method of computer storage of seismic data is illustrated together with some typical seismograms from recent large earthquakes.

Next we pose two questions:

> How can seismograms be used to determine the source of a seismic event?

> How do we obtain information about the Earth's interior from travel times?

First some features of deeply penetrating earthquake waves, with long source–receiver distances, are used to show that the core–mantle boundary can be located through the strong seismic refractions that occur at depths of 2 900 km inside the Earth (details are given in Section 4). Then the principle of determining the distance between the source of a seismic event and the recording station using the delay time between P- and S-waves (see Figure 25) is discussed. When several such distance estimates have been made, the source (focus) of an event can be located by triangulation. Data for short event–receiver distances are useful for determining the shallow structure of the Earth because the depth of penetration along the wave path is small (Figure 34), and evidence for the crust–mantle refracting boundary is obtained from such events. Artificially generated seismograms, produced by explosions and vibrosonics (heavy truck-mounted vibrating concrete slabs) are widely used for even shallower prospecting (e.g. in the oil and coal industry). The Newbury observatory was established, together with its sensitive instrumentation and high-powered computer facilities, to record and distinguish between nuclear explosions and natural earthquakes; examples from the USSR are illustrated in the programme.

We then return to the simulation table at the University of Bristol to show how the design of earthquake-resistant buildings has been greatly improved by engineering tests on model structures. The programme ends with a brief summary of recent theories of the mechanisms of earthquakes, on which some methods for predicting future seismic events have been based (with varying degrees of success!).

You are now in a position to apply your knowledge of the physical characteristics of seismic waves to help to construct a model for the structure and composition of the Earth's interior. The other primary source of data used to compile this model is that of the Earth's magnetism which we introduce in the next Section as a prelude to developing the model, using both seismic and magnetic data, in Section 4.

SUMMARY OF SECTION 2

1   Seismic disturbances, generated by earthquakes, result in the transmission of energy through the ground in the form of wave-like vibrations. The waves propagate through elastic media so they cause only temporary deformation of the material through which they pass, without producing any permanent change.

2   Seismic waves which pass *through* the Earth are of two types: P-waves and S-waves.

P-waves are compressional waves that disturb the medium by changing its volume in the direction of propagation, without changing its basic shape. Their speeds (magnitudes of their velocities) are related to the axial modulus and the density of Earth materials as follows:

$$v_P = \sqrt{\psi/\rho}$$

S-waves are transverse or shear waves that disturb the medium by changing its shape at right angles to the direction of propagation without changing its volume. Their speeds are related to the rigidity modulus and the density of Earth materials as follows:

$$v_S = \sqrt{\mu/\rho}$$

Liquids have effectively zero resistance to shear and so do not transmit S-waves.

3   When a seismic wave passes from a rock layer with higher seismic speed to one with lower seismic speed, its *velocity* changes (i.e. both its speed and its direction of motion change). The wave is refracted towards the normal at the boundary between the two layers, according to Snell's law:

$$\frac{\sin i}{\sin r} = \frac{v_1}{v_2}$$

4   When seismic waves pass from rocks with lower seismic wave speed into rocks with higher seismic speed, most of the energy of the waves is refracted

along paths away from the normal according to Snell's law, up to a certain angle of incidence called the critical angle:

$$\sin i_c = \frac{v_1}{v_2}$$

At the critical angle, there is still a refracted wave which travels closely parallel to the boundary within the high-speed layer but, at higher angles of incidence, waves are totally reflected within the low-speed layer.

5   Where the seismic wave speed of rocks changes continuously with depth, earthquake waves undergo continuous refraction.

6   If an earthquake occurs in a medium with low seismic wave speed surrounded by layers with higher seismic wave speed much of the energy will be trapped by internal reflections within the low-speed layer.

SAQ 6   (a) Which of the following statements (i)–(v) are true?

(b) Which one of the true statements in (a) correctly explains why S-waves cannot be transmitted through liquids?

(i)   Liquids are easily compressible.
(ii) Liquids are not elastic materials when subject to shear.
(iii) The density of liquids increases when compressed.
(iv) Liquids have very high rigidity moduli.
(v)   Liquids have very low axial moduli.

SAQ 7   A typical granite (such as specimen S1 in your Experiment Kit) near the surface of the Earth has a density of $2.7 \times 10^3 \, \text{kg m}^{-3}$, and axial and rigidity moduli of $8.5 \times 10^{10} \, \text{N m}^{-2}$ and $3.0 \times 10^{10} \, \text{N m}^{-2}$ respectively. Calculate, in units of km s^{-1}, the speeds of P-waves and S-waves in granite.

SAQ 8   Which two of the following statements about wave speeds in rocks are correct?

(a) P-wave speed increases if density increases and axial modulus is fixed.

T (b) P-wave speed increases if axial modulus increases and density is fixed.

T (c) S-wave speed increases if density decreases and rigidity modulus is fixed.

(d) S-wave speed decreases if rigidity modulus increases and density is fixed.

(e) P- and S-wave speeds decrease if the corresponding elastic moduli increase faster than the density increases.

SAQ 9   Calculate the angle of refraction of a P-wave which has an angle of incidence of $30°$ on crossing a boundary from rock with $v_1 = 6.3 \, \text{km s}^{-1}$ into rock with $v_2 = 8.2 \, \text{km s}^{-1}$.

SAQ 10   Select from the equations (a)–(d) below the correct relationship between the angle of incidence i and the angle of reflection R:

(a) $i = \sin R$ (c) $\sin i \times \sin R$ is constant

(b) $\sin i = R$ (d) $i = R$

SAQ 11   Will a P-wave travelling in a rock with a speed of $4.5 \, \text{km s}^{-1}$ be refracted, reflected or both, on meeting a boundary with a rock in which the wave speed is $5.5 \, \text{km s}^{-1}$, if the angle of incidence is $60°$?

SAQ 12   Look at Figure 36. In what way must seismic wave speed change with depth for a seismic wave to follow a path through the layers A and B of the form shown in the Figure?

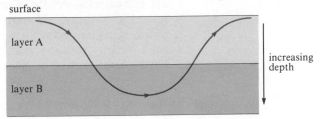

FIGURE 36   Wave path through layers A and B (for use with SAQ 12).

39

3 THE EARTH AS A MAGNET

You now know enough to realize that the travel times of seismic waves can provide some essential clues about the Earth's internal structure and composition. In this Section, we are going to introduce another phenomenon, the Earth's magnetism, which is useful in a similar way because it originates *inside* the Earth, yet is observable *at the surface*.

3.1 A FIRST LOOK AT THE EARTH'S MAGNETISM

Although it was poorly understood until the 20th century and is still far from fully understood, the Earth's magnetism has been used since ancient times. The ancients first came across magnetism in the form of **lodestone**, a naturally occurring magnetic rock. Lodestone is so strongly magnetic that it can be used to pick up small pieces of iron as well as other fragments of lodestone. It was known to the Greeks by at least 600 BC; and by the first century AD the Chinese had used it to construct the first compass in the form of a lodestone spoon balanced on a smooth plate (Figure 37).

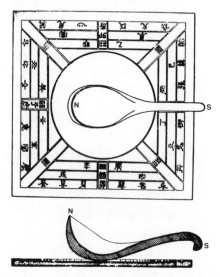

FIGURE 37   Model lodestone spoon and bronze plate reconstructed during the 1940s from an ancient Chinese pattern. This is the earliest form of the magnetic compass. The handle of the spoon points approximately south.

As long as a lodestone spoon of the shape shown is free to rotate, it will always come to rest in an approximately north–south direction because it is influenced by the direction of the Earth's magnetism. The Chinese did not recognize this influence; indeed, it was not until 1600 AD, when William Gilbert, a London physician, showed that the behaviour of a compass needle at the Earth's surface was very similar to that of an iron needle placed on the surface of a lodestone sphere, that people began to realize that magnetism may be one of the Earth's most fundamental properties. By 1726, this concept was familiar to no less an author than Jonathan Swift who, in *Gulliver's Travels*, had the island of Laputa, which contained an enormous pivoting block of lodestone, powered by magnetic forces. Systematic measurements of the effect of the Earth's magnetism were begun in the early 19th century and were then limited to the Earth's surface and the restricted regions immediately below it made accessible by mining. Much more recently, aviation and space flight have allowed measurements of the Earth's magnetism to be made far out into space.

If a chart is plotted showing the direction in which a compass needle sets at various points in the space around the Earth, it looks like Figure 38. This diagram has a striking feature which suggests that the origin of the pattern must be inside the Earth rather than external to it (on the Sun or Moon, for example).

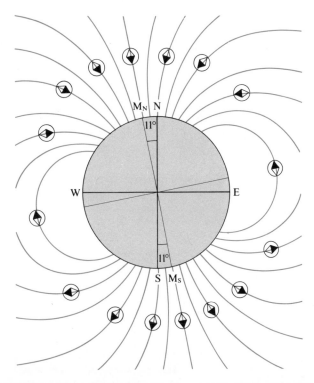

FIGURE 38   The pattern of the Earth's magnetic field outside the Earth's surface. N and S are the geographic north and south poles, respectively. The magnetic field pattern is symmetrical about the Earth's centre but inclined at $11°$ to the rotational axis. M_N and M_S, the geomagnetic poles, are the points where the axis of the magnetic field cuts the Earth's surface in the Northern and Southern Hemispheres, respectively. The shaded halves of the compass needles are the north poles and point towards M_N.

☐ What is this feature?

■ The pattern is symmetrical about the Earth's centre, a feature which would be most unlikely to occur if the magnetic source were located outside the Earth!

Notice, however, that the pattern is not quite symmetrical about the Earth's axis of rotation (the line joining the north and south geographic poles). Instead, it is symmetrical about a line sloping at an angle of $11°$ to the axis of rotation, and this is a feature we shall consider later. Before we go any further with our examination of the Earth's magnetism we need to consider some general properties of magnets, and that is why we have provided some equipment for you to carry out simple magnetic experiments at home.

3.2 AN INTRODUCTION TO MAGNETISM

You may well be familiar with most of the basic properties of magnets, but the following two experiments and associated text are important and are intended to help you to check your understanding of magnetism.

EXPERIMENT 1   THE MAGNETIC FORCES DUE TO A BAR MAGNET

TIME

This experiment takes about 15 minutes.

NON-KIT ITEMS

sheet of A4 paper (preferably plain)

two books of roughly the same size, both about 1 cm thick

fairly large firm horizontal surface on which to work (well away from large pieces of iron and steel: a large wooden table is ideal)

KIT ITEMS

Part 1

bar magnet

iron filings

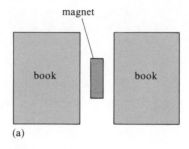

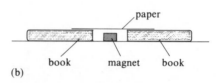

FIGURE 39   Arrangement of items for Experiment 1: (a) seen from above, (b) seen end-on and with the sheet of A4 paper in position.

METHOD

Take the bar magnet and place it on the flat horizontal surface, making sure the other magnet is well away from your experiment. Place the two books at either side of the magnet as shown in Figure 39a and then cover the magnet with a sheet of A4 paper centred over the magnet (Figure 39b).

During the next operation, try to avoid letting the iron filings come into direct contact with the magnet since they are very difficult to remove from the magnet if they get attached.

Now take the packet of iron filings and gently sprinkle them with your fingers onto the surface of the paper from a height of 10 cm or so, starting around the centre. Try to spread the filings out as evenly as possible.

Make a sketch in your Notebook of the *pattern* made by the iron filings. (The pattern may be easier to see if you tap the paper gently once or twice.)

ITQ 16   Describe precisely from the pattern you have just sketched the general 'shape' of the magnetic forces due to the bar magnet, both near the ends, and elsewhere.

Whatever the *nature* of the forces that produced the patterns you have just observed, this experiment does suggest some general features of the magnetic force in the vicinity of a bar magnet:

(i)   It is strongest at the ends of the magnet.

(ii)   At the sides it is weaker and parallel to the length of the magnet.

(iii) It is three-dimensional—this is why the filings point down into the paper over the ends of the magnet. (If you are not yet convinced about this point you soon will be, for we demonstrate the effect in the TV programme 'Magnetic Earth'.)

EXPERIMENT CONTINUED

The pattern of the magnetic forces you sketched will look something like Figure 40a, which is a two-dimensional representation of the three-dimensional pattern of forces shown in Figure 40b. This pattern of lines represents a model of the orientation of forces in three dimensions in the vicinity of a bar magnet.

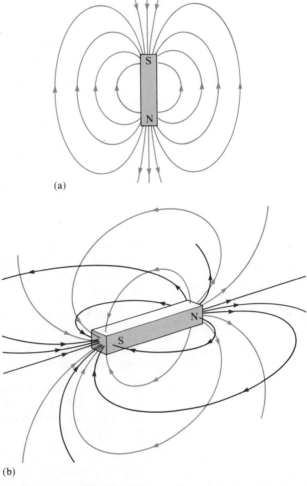

(a)

(b)

FIGURE 40   (a) Two-dimensional representation of the magnetic forces around a bar magnet; (b) simplified three-dimensional representation of the same force field showing the field lines in the horizontal and vertical planes only (black curves and red curves, respectively).

When you have convinced yourself about this, carefully remove the paper and return the iron filings to the packet, but keep your experimental equipment to hand—you will need it again soon.

FIELD OF FORCE

MAGNETIC FIELD

Now when an object acts by some force on other objects in the space around it, we say that those objects are in a **field of force** (field, for short). At each point in the field, the magnitude and the direction of the force can be measured using a suitable test object and measuring instrument. The field is very often represented graphically (modelled) by *lines of force* (Figure 40) which are sometimes called field lines. The *direction* of the lines gives the direction of the force at each particular point. Their *density* gives an indication about the magnitude of the force in the area of the field around the point. So the lines of force shown in Figure 40b give a full graphical representation of the **magnetic field** of a bar magnet.

Look back to Figure 38: now you can see that this Figure is a graphical representation (model) of the magnetic field of the Earth.

NORTH POLE OF A MAGNET

SOUTH POLE OF A MAGNET

GEOMAGNETIC POLES

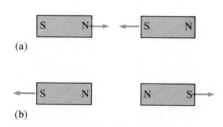

(a)

(b)

FIGURE 41 Interactions of bar magnets. In (a) the force between the magnets is attractive; in (b) it is repulsive. The arrows indicate the directions of the forces experienced by each magnet.

☐ What other terrestrial phenomenon have you come across in the Course so far that must also have a field of force?

■ We are, of course, referring to the gravitational attraction of one body by another (see Unit 3); the Earth has a strong gravitational field that is responsible for holding us down to its surface.

But whereas the gravitational field of the Earth produces acceleration that is directed vertically downwards everywhere, the magnetic field is much more complicated, as you can see from Figure 38. In this cross-section of the Earth there are only two places, over the magnetic 'poles', where the compass needles point either vertically downwards or upwards.

Clearly, there is a remarkable similarity between the field of a bar magnet and the magnetic field of the Earth. This suggests that, to a first approximation, we can think of the Earth as if it had a bar magnet inside, with two ends (the places where the field lines are focused, known as *poles*) defining the axis of symmetry of the field. Before going any further, we must introduce the correct terminology for describing the relationship of the Earth's *magnetic* poles to its *geographic* poles.

The starting point is the *geographic north pole*, which is unambiguously defined by the position of Polaris (Unit 1). The next step is to define the end of the magnetic needle in a navigation compass (used in navigation for determining directions relative to north) as the *north pole of the compass*. The magnetic needle in a navigation compass is simply a bar magnet and we know that all bar magnets have two different poles. They are named according to how they act on a compass needle or another bar magnet (Figure 41), as follows:

The **south pole of a magnet** is the one that *attracts* the north pole of a compass or bar magnet (as defined above).

The **north pole of a magnet** is the one that *repels* the north pole of a compass or bar magnet.

The present orientation of the Earth's magnetic field is such that the *south* magnetic pole is located in the Northern Hemisphere and so attracts the north pole of the compass. However, this has not always been the case, as you will see later.

There is, unfortunately, a lot of confusion in most geological and geographical texts generated by the name 'north magnetic pole' being used for the magnetic pole which lies in the Northern Hemisphere. For scientific consistency, this pole can only be called 'south magnetic pole', but this would be an odd juxtaposition with geographic north. To avoid this confusion, we shall call the place towards which a compass needle points, the **geomagnetic pole in the north** (M_N in Figure 38), and the place away from which a compass needle points, the **geomagnetic pole in the south** (M_S).

Now you are ready to carry out the second experiment which will reinforce your understanding of magnetic poles and fields. We shall then return to our description of the Earth's magnetic field.

EXPERIMENT 2   THE POLES AND FIELD OF A BAR MAGNET

TIME
This experiment takes about 25 minutes.

NON-KIT ITEMS
A4 paper (one sheet)
pair of compasses (to draw a circle)
ruler
Sellotape or Blu-Tack

KIT ITEMS
Part 1
bar magnet
compass

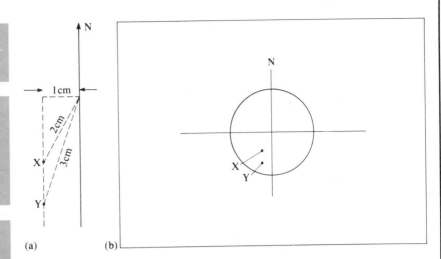

FIGURE 42   Preparation of an A4 sheet of paper for Experiment 2: (a) construction of points X and Y (actual dimensions); (b) plan of paper (reduced scale).

METHOD

First of all, you will need to find out which pole of the bar magnet is the south pole. You can do this quite simply by finding the pole of the magnet which attracts the *north* pole of the compass needle i.e. the pointed, arrowed end. (You should check that this is the north pole of your compass needle by making sure that it does point roughly towards the north.) When you have done this, use a pencil to mark the south pole of the magnet with the letter S. Now draw a line of length about 10 cm across the width of the sheet of A4 paper, centred on the middle, and mark one end of the line with the letter N.

Mark the midpoint of the line you have just drawn, and then draw a circle of radius about 4 cm centred on this point. Next, mark two points X and Y which are, respectively, 2 cm and 3 cm from the centre point of the line, away from the end marked N, and 1 cm from the line itself (Figure 42a). Finally draw a straight line at right angles to the first line and through the midpoint of this line, to cut the circle you have drawn. You should now have a piece of paper looking like Figure 42b.

With the magnets well out of the way, put the compass at the centre of the circle. The compass needle will point north. Now, keeping the compass fixed, turn the sheet of paper so that the end of the line marked with an N also points exactly towards the north. Use Sellotape or Blu-Tack to stick the sheet down to your table so that the paper cannot be moved.

Remove the compass, and put the magnet on the paper along the line with the centre of the line at the centre of the magnet, and the *south* pole of the magnet pointing *north* i.e. towards the point N on the paper.

Now you are ready to map out the magnetic field. Put the compass so that the south end of the needle is on the dot marked X, and make another dot next to the north end of the needle (the arrow end). Now put the south end of the needle over the new dot, and repeat the process (Figure 43). Continue until the line of dots that results brings the compass back near the magnet, at a similar distance to that at which you started.

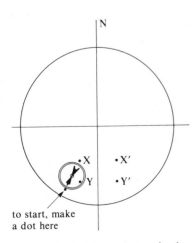

FIGURE 43   How to start plotting field lines in Experiment 2.

EXPERIMENT CONTINUED

Join the points together in a smooth curve and mark the curve with an arrow to show the direction in which the north pole of the compass pointed.

Now repeat this whole process, starting at point Y.

You may repeat the process again for a number of starting points; it would be particularly helpful to attempt to draw field lines starting at the equivalent points, X' and Y', on the right-hand side of your circle (see Figure 43).

Now clear away the experiment, but keep the magnets and compass handy for another short experiment that you will be doing near the end of Section 3.

ITQ 17 (a) Do your arrows on the curves point along the curves towards or away from the points X and Y?

(b) Is the angle where the curve through X meets the circle the same as the angle where the curve through Y meets the circle?

You have just plotted the shape of the magnetic field around a bar magnet in cross-section and this resembles the two-dimensional model illustrated in Figure 40a. In case you were wondering whether the Earth's field had any effect on the shape of the field which you have just plotted, let us just say for the moment that the alignment of the bar magnet, with the south pole of the magnet pointing north, was carefully chosen so that the general shape of the field lines resulting from the magnet is very similar to that which you would have found if the Earth's field had been absent. Furthermore, within 10 cm or so of the magnet, the effect of the Earth's field is small in relation to that of the magnet and so has only a small effect on the shape of the magnet's field, regardless of the magnet's orientation.

We are now in a position to combine the results of the two experiments with bar magnets by extending into three dimensions your observations of the way lines of force cut a circle around a bar magnet, using the model deduced from Experiment 1 and illustrated in Figure 40b.

ITQ 18 If you were given a plastic sphere with a bar magnet symmetrical about the centre and aligned vertically, would you expect the direction of the magnetic field to make the same angle to the surface of the sphere at all points on the sphere's surface? If not, how will the angle vary from the top of the sphere, above one end of the magnet, round to the bottom?

We can now return to our examination of the Earth's magnetic field. If we take a cross-section through the sphere in ITQ 18 which includes the north and south poles of the sphere and magnet, then the field of force will look like Figure 44. How similar is this to the Earth's magnetic field, shown in Figure 38? In other words: How similar is the Earth's field to that of a large bar magnet?

MAGNETIC DIPOLE

AXIALLY GEOCENTRIC
DIPOLE

3.3 DESCRIBING THE EARTH'S MAGNETIC FIELD

It will be clear to you by now that the simplest possible magnetic field that the Earth could have is that of a bar magnet which, unlike that in Figure 44, is inclined at about 11° to the axis of rotation. The field is essentially that of a **magnetic dipole**; in other words it is associated with *two poles*, like a bar magnet. No one has yet observed an isolated pole, whether north or south. For the moment, let us make a simplifying assumption and consider the characteristics of the field produced by a dipole lying at the centre of the Earth and aligned along the Earth's rotational axis. This is called an **axially geocentric dipole**, which is exactly as shown in Figure 44. We have defined the places towards and away from which compass needles point as the *geomagnetic poles*: M_N in the Northern Hemisphere and M_S in the Southern Hemisphere.

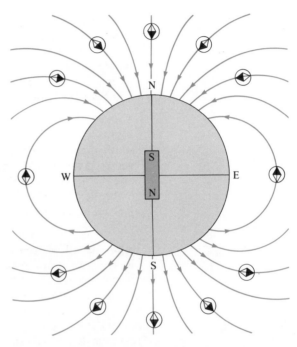

FIGURE 44   Field lines (red) with compass needles oriented correctly (cf. Figure 38) around a bar magnet located at the centre of a sphere. The geographic directions N, S, E, W are marked for ease of comparison with Figure 38.

□ Where are the geomagnetic poles M_N and M_S located in an axially geocentric dipole model of the Earth's magnetic field?

■ Since *in this model* the dipole axis and rotation axis coincide, M_N and M_S coincide, respectively, with the north and south geographic poles.

Now imagine that you are standing on the Equator (i.e. the geographic equator) with an ordinary compass and that you walk along a line of longitude from the Equator towards the north geographic pole.

□ Which way will the north pole of the compass needle point as you travel?

■ Clearly, throughout, it will stay pointing towards the geomagnetic pole M_N (which, in our model in Figure 44, is also the north geographic pole).

But look again at Figure 44—the compass needles are not pointing directly north but along their respective field lines down into or up from inside the Earth. However, ordinary compasses measure only that part of the field which can be sensed in a *horizontal* plane: this is called the horizontal *component* of the magnetic field. If you were to use a special kind of compass with a horizontal axis that allowed the needle to rotate *vertically* you would get a different result.

MAGNETIC INCLINATION

MAGNETIC DECLINATION

☐ Imagine that using such a vertical compass needle you start from the Equator and walk north along a line of longitude: what will happen to this needle?

■ It will set horizontally at the Equator, pointing due north, and it will dip down towards the Earth's surface at an ever-increasing angle as you travel north until at the north geographic pole, the location of M_N in our model, it points vertically downwards. This result is illustrated in Figure 44.

You can see from Figure 44 that the direction of the field lines becomes ever more steep as you approach the poles; similarly in the Southern Hemisphere, the needle would point upwards at an angle that increases as we move south, becoming vertical again at the south geographic pole, the site of M_S in this model.

The angle that the needle makes with the horizontal is called the **magnetic inclination** and is said to be positive if the north pole of the needle dips below the horizontal and negative if it rises above the horizontal. With the simple geocentric axial dipole in Figure 44 the inclination is positive everywhere in the Northern Hemisphere and negative everywhere in the Southern Hemisphere.

You could make a rough estimate of magnetic inclination by using the compass in your Kit. Turn it vertically, set it with the needle in a north–south direction (which you should know from Experiment 2) and tap it gently. You should find the needle pointing downwards at an angle of about 70°. In the TV programme, we also show you a measurement of magnetic inclination being made at a point closer to the North Pole, in Iceland, where the value is 77°.

Let us now return to the situation shown in Figure 38 where the Earth's dipole is still geocentric but no longer coincides with the axis of rotation. Remember, as you read on, that this is also a simplifying assumption; there is one more stage of complexity to which we will introduce you later. One consequence of the sloping of the dipole with respect to the axis of rotation is that the geomagnetic and geographic poles no longer coincide. The points at which the dipole axis cuts the Earth's surface (i.e. the geomagnetic poles in the Northern and Southern Hemispheres, M_N and M_S) lie, in the section shown in Figure 38, 11° of latitude away from the geographic poles.

In order to intersect all four poles, a special section through the Earth must be taken (i.e. along two particular lines of longitude, in fact along 70° W–110° E) and, for the moment, we can define the geomagnetic poles as follows: M_N is located at 79° N, 70° W and M_S at 79° S, 110° E.

Now we have an interesting situation. Imagine yourself at the Equator again, walking north—and, for simplicity, you had better walk from the west along the 70° W line of longitude towards the north geographic pole.

☐ What will happen to your horizontal axis compass needle if it is free to move vertically?

■ At the Equator (W in Figure 38), the needle will not lie horizontally but will point into the ground a little below the horizontal. As you move from the Equator to the north geographic pole, the inclination will increase until you reach M_N but will subsequently decrease again.

☐ What would happen to a normal horizontal compass (i.e. with a vertical axis) along the same line?

■ It would point towards both the north geomagnetic and geographic poles until you pass M_N but then it should point back, 180° away from geographic north.

Not surprisingly, this can play havoc with navigation, especially in polar regions. But it is a complication elsewhere too. This is because you have just considered a special section through the Earth that cuts both the geomagnetic and geographic poles; elsewhere, for example at a midpoint on the Equator between W and E on Figure 38, there is an angle between the directions of geomagnetic and geographic north. So, normal compass needles rarely point in the direction you might expect! The angle between the apparent directions of geomagnetic and geographic north is called the **magnetic declination** and it is reckoned as degrees east or west of true, or geographic north. Figure 45 illustrates the relationship between magnetic inclination, magnetic declination and geographic north for a point on the Earth's surface.

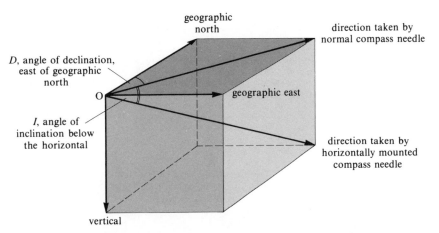

FIGURE 45 Schematic illustration of magnetic inclination I and declination D for a point O on the Earth's surface. Note that the horizontal is in the plane between geographic north and east.

☐ Is the point O in Figure 45 in the Northern or Southern Hemisphere?

■ Because the inclination points downwards at a sizeable angle, it must be well within the Northern Hemisphere.

In addition, point O must be further west than 70° W because the declination is east of true north. (Don't worry if this point is elusive—it is rather subtle!)

You might think that our description of the Earth's magnetic field has now become quite complicated enough, and we would sympathize with this view. Unfortunately there is one final stage of complication that we need to introduce at this point in order to satisfy our aim of using the magnetic field to find out about the Earth's interior. One of the most fascinating aspects of the field is that it cannot *quite* be explained in terms of a simple dipole source way down inside the Earth. For example, look at Figure 46 (overleaf); it is not quite what we would expect if the Earth's field were a simple dipole.

Figure 46 is a contour map of the Earth's *magnetic field strength* for 1985. Each contour joins up all the places on the Earth's surface where the field strength has a particular value. The rectangular grid is of north–south lines of longitude and east–west lines of latitude; notice the latter are stretched out towards the geographic poles (which do not appear on the projection). Although we do not need to go into the details of how magnetic field strength can be determined, it should be clear that the size of magnetic forces is related to field strength which can be measured through its effect on test objects. The SI unit used to measure the strength of magnetic fields

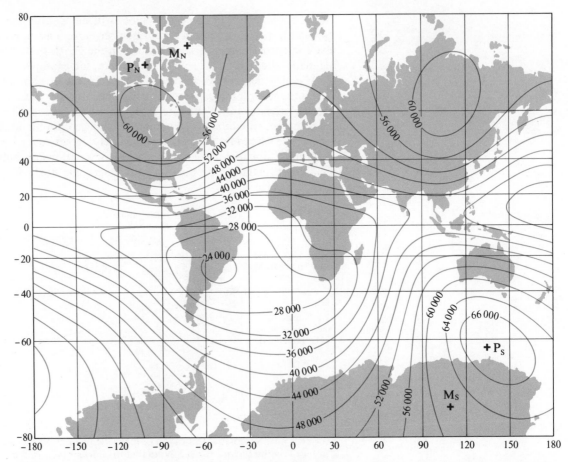

FIGURE 46   Map showing lines of equal geomagnetic field strength for the year 1985; the units are nanoteslas ($1\,nT = 10^{-9}\,T$). M_N and M_S are the geomagnetic poles and the positions P_N and P_S are the magnetic dip poles, which are discussed later in the text.

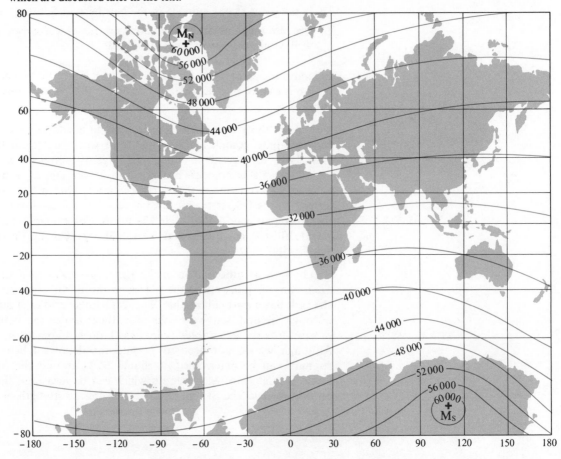

FIGURE 47   Map showing the intensity (units: nT) of a purely dipole field with the same pole positions M_N and M_S as in Figure 46 and plotted on the same scale.

NON-DIPOLE COMPONENT OF THE EARTH'S MAGNETIC FIELD

TESLA

is called the **tesla**, for which the abbreviation is T. To give you some idea of the relative magnitudes (i.e. strengths) of magnetic fields, the Earth's field strength at the surface is normally between 10^{-4} and 10^{-5} T whilst a bar magnet like the ones in the Kit produces a field strength of around 10^{-1} T near its ends. The units in Figure 46 are nanoteslas ($1\,nT = 10^{-9}$ T) and the largest contour value, occurring at about 60° S, 140° E, is 66 000 nT (6.6×10^{-5} T).

Now the magnetic field produced by a magnet generally varies by a factor of rather more than two, increasing from the magnetic equator (i.e. the region around the midpoint of the magnet) to the poles; and it is related in a simple way to the concentration of lines of force, as represented in Figure 40. That means we would expect the strength of the Earth's magnetism, if it were simply dipolar, to increase regularly, as we move from the magnetic equator to the geomagnetic poles. Bearing in mind the 11° inclination of the dipole axis, the map of field strength should, according to the simple dipole model, look like Figure 47 with approximately circular field strength contours around the two geomagnetic poles. On a sphere the contours would all be circular, including the one that represents minimum field strength around the magnetic equator. On the projection in Figure 47 the circles open out and the magnetic equator is represented by a gentle curved line sloping across the Figure because of the north–west to south–east inclination of the dipole axis relative to the Earth's axis of rotation.

ITQ 19 (a) Describe, in a few sentences, the general variation of field strength over the Earth's surface (Figure 46). Concentrate on areas where field strength is higher or lower than average.

(b) How well does this field strength map support the simple dipole model for the Earth's magnetic field shown in Figure 47?

It follows from ITQ 19 that the Earth's field is mainly dipolar but the analysis of a wide range of geomagnetic data, such as those illustrated in Figure 46, show that there are non-dipolar components which can be isolated from the dipolar component. The simplest way of looking at this is to say that in addition to the dipole field there is a **non-dipole field component** which is irregular, and it is this smaller component which accounts for irregularities such as the differences between Figures 46 and 47.

☐ Since the non-dipole component represents only a small part of the total field, which modifies slightly the appearance of the dipole field, how can the non-dipole field be isolated mathematically?

■ The dipole field is subtracted from the total field to reveal the non-dipole component.

In fact, that is a reasonable description of the process whereby the *best-fitting* dipole is subtracted from all the observations for a particular time in order to reveal the shape and size of the non-dipole component. Mathematically we can express this as: non-dipole component = total field − dipole component. Figure 48 (overleaf) shows contour maps of the non-dipole component.

Concentrate on Figure 48a (ignore Figure 48b for the moment—we shall need this later) and do not worry about the fact that this is a 'vertical' component map—this is just a convenient way of looking at an irregular field. You will see that the non-dipole field component forms a series of high (positive) and low (negative) centres. These are places where the non-dipole component is positive and negative (respectively) with respect to the dipole component. Thus, for example, the low at A over the Atlantic between Africa and South America reaches −16 000 nT whereas the high over the USSR and China reaches 16 000 nT. Notice that these are two of the areas where the dipole model (Figure 47) fits the observed field (Figure 46) least well (ITQ 19b). The coincidence between the highs and lows in Figures 46 and 48a is inexact because different field components are shown.

Do not spend time worrying about this; the important point is that, in some areas, the non-dipole field component can be a large proportion of the total. However, *on average*, the non-dipole component is only about 5% of the total magnetic field.

So the 'centres' of the non-dipole field are causing the disturbances from the regular patterns we should expect of a simple dipole. Now, of course, when the magnetic inclination I of the total field is measured at the two places we have identified as the geomagnetic poles M_N and M_S (shown in Figure 46), it is found not to be 90°. Once again, we find the magnetic poles do not behave quite as we had expected.

☐ How can you account for this additional discrepancy?

■ Again this is because the non-dipole field component is causing the field to be distorted away from that of a dipole. The inclination at the geomagnetic poles is the net result of the 90° dipolar inclination and the disturbance due to the non-dipole component.

The revised positions of the poles P_N and P_S (shown in Figure 46) are the points where the dipole and non-dipole fields just balanced in 1985 in such a way that the net inclination was vertical. These are called the **magnetic dip poles** and are of considerable historical interest; many expeditions in the 19th century set off to look for these poles and many became confused by the obvious difficulties of navigating in their vicinity! They are distinct from the geomagnetic poles (M_N and M_S in Figure 46) we have been describing so far in that the *dip poles can actually be detected on the ground* whereas M_N and M_S are really the mathematical 'best-fit' positions of the dipole field axis where it cuts the Earth's surface. Of course, the dip poles are not antipodal (i.e. exactly opposite points on the Earth's surface) because the non-dipole field is irregular and very different in each hemisphere.

3.4 CHANGES IN THE EARTH'S MAGNETIC FIELD

We now come to the climax of Section 3 and examine some of the most exciting discoveries made in the subject of terrestrial magnetism, discoveries that tell us a great deal about the nature of the magnetic field source that exists within the Earth.

As long ago as 1635, Henry Gellibrand presented his discovery that, between 1580 and 1634, the magnetic declination at London had changed from 11.3° E to 4.1° E. This was the first time that anyone had noticed that the Earth's magnetic field was not static, although it has to be admitted that the only systematic observations up to that time were of magnetic declination and inclination, and that these early measurements were hardly the ultimate in accuracy. Subsequent observers found, especially after systematic measurements were begun early in the 19th century, that *all the features of the Earth's magnetic field change with time*. These changes are known as **secular variations** ('secular' as used here merely means 'time').

3.4.I DIRECT OBSERVATIONS OF THE EARTH'S MAGNETISM

So far as the geomagnetic dipole is concerned, throughout the period of direct observation, the field has been essentially dipolar, but the axis of the dipole has moved a little. For example, during the last 130 years or so, the geomagnetic pole M_N has remained at a latitude of about 79° N but has moved in longitude from about 64° W to about 70° W—a rate of change of about *0.042° longitude a year*. While this change in dipole orientation may not be spectacular, the change in field *strength* over the same time has been

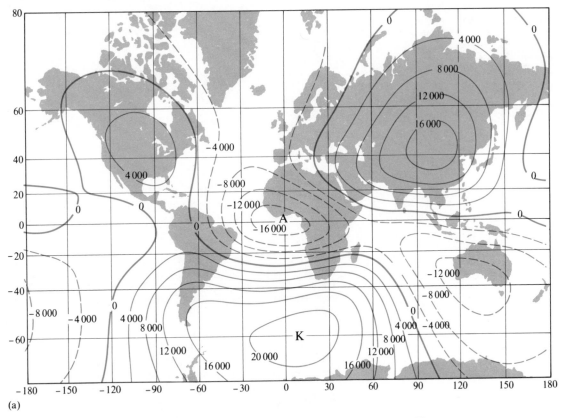

(a)

FIGURE 48   (a) The vertical component of the non-dipole field for 1985 (units: nT).

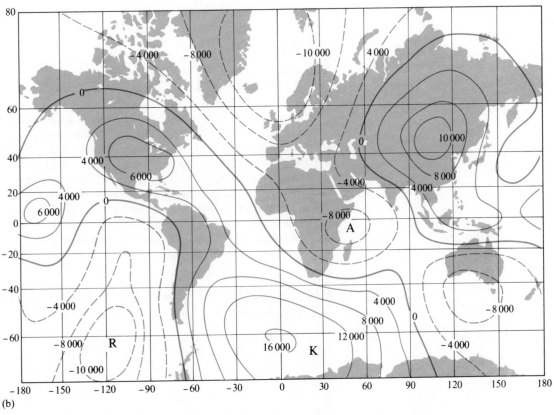

(b)

FIGURE 48   (b) The vertical component of the non-dipole field for 1835 (units: nT).

much more dramatic. Since about 1800, it has been decreasing more or less linearly at a rate of about 5% *per century* all over the Earth's surface (Figure 49).

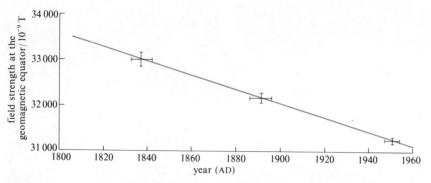

FIGURE 49 Changes in the geomagnetic field strength at the geomagnetic equator. The points are the average values of all determinations within the 50-year intervals 1815–1865, 1865–1915 and 1915–1965, respectively. The vertical bars represent the uncertainties in the experimental data used to calculate the average values.

By contrast, the non-dipole field component has been changing much more rapidly. Now is the time to compare its appearance in 1835 (Figure 48b) with that in 1985 (Figure 48a, which you have studied already).

☐ What are the main differences between Figures 48a and 48b? Look, in particular, at centres A, K on both maps and at centre R on the 1835 map.

■ Centre A in 1835 lay to the east of Africa and had a non-dipole field of magnitude −8 000 nT, but by 1985 it had moved to the east of South America and had changed to −16 000 nT. Centre K grew by about 4 000 nT over the same period. Centre R on the 1835 map had totally disappeared by 1985.

These examples illustrate some very important properties of the non-dipole field component. It is continuously changing. On average, when the full record is studied in detail, it turns out that the whole field component is drifting westward at a rate of about *0.2° longitude a year*. This seems to imply that if it were to persist long enough, it would move right around the world in about 1 800 years. In fact, it does not persist in one form for that long. The centres are continuously changing—growing, diminishing, expanding, contracting and disappearing and reappearing, as you will see in animated form in the TV programme 'Magnetic Earth'. The amounts of time over which these changes appear to take place are of the order of $10–10^3$ years. By comparison, it appears that the dipole field changes much more slowly, over time-scales of about 10^4 years. There are some indirect measurements of the magnetic field made *before* the period of direct observations which support this view.

3.4.2 INDIRECT MEASUREMENT OF THE EARTH'S PAST GEOMAGNETIC FIELD

Over the past 30 years, many questions about the older history of the Earth's magnetic field have been answered, thanks to a remarkable discovery actually made in the 19th century but only recently developed. The discovery was that many rocks preserve the direction and magnitude of the geomagnetic field at the time they are formed—in other words, the magnetism becomes 'locked inside' the rocks when, for example, igneous magmas crystallize. The study of the magnetization of rocks is called **palaeomagnetism** (*palaios* is the Greek word for 'old'). As you will see in Section 5 and in the TV programme, these methods have been used to investigate the positions of the magnetic poles well back in time beyond the period of direct observation.

Although the technique has been applied successfully to determine the Earth's magnetic field characteristics in rocks several thousand million years old, here we shall concentrate only on the last few thousand years. Figure 50 provides data on the changing position of the **palaeomagnetic pole** in the Northern Hemisphere from rocks up to 7 000 years old. Before you go any further, read the caption carefully so that you know the positions of the geographic pole and the present geomagnetic pole, and so that you understand what the plot means. Note also that in dealing with palaeomagnetism it is impossible to distinguish between the geomagnetic poles of a theoretical dipole (M_N and M_S) and the dip poles (P_N and P_S). We must make the simplifying assumption that they are coincident and, as you will see, this causes no problems in interpreting the data. Moreover, many different samples have been measured in order to obtain the average pole positions for each point in Figure 50.

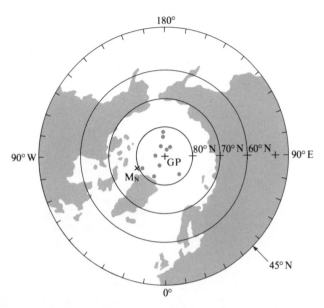

FIGURE 50   The positions of the palaeomagnetic pole in the Northern Hemisphere (red spots) at different points in time during the last 7 000 years. Imagine that you are looking down on the Earth from a point directly above the north geographic pole (GP) which is therefore in the centre of the diagram. The pole positions are thus plotted exactly as you would see them. The cross (×) to the left of and just below GP is the position of the present geomagnetic pole M_N (see Figures 38 and 46). Notice that the outer circle is the 45° N line of latitude; the area between 45° N and the Equator, which you would see from your vantage point, has been omitted for clarity. (*Note:*   Each of the palaeomagnetic pole positions shown is an average for many rock samples. In each case, therefore, any random fluctuations there may be due to the non-dipole field component have been effectively removed.)

Given the time-variant nature of the geomagnetic field described above for the last 160 years or so, you might be surprised to learn that the geomagnetic poles have always been within about 11° of the geographic poles—at least for the last 7 000 years—yet that is what Figure 50 shows. But notice something else quite important. The poles are not scattered around the present geomagnetic pole but about the geographic pole. Thus, it seems that the geomagnetic field has, *on average*, been that of an axial dipole! The observation that the maximum deviation of the geomagnetic poles from the geographic poles is about 11° tells us that they do not wander much further than that. This slight variation in the dipole direction is known as **dipole wobble** and as with field strength it appears to have a period of around 10^4 years.

Even more convincing evidence of this periodicity has been derived through palaeomagnetic investigations of archaeological materials which yield data on ancient field *strengths*. The technique is now only in its infancy and is subject to much less uncertainty when applied to fire bricks and pottery, baked by ancient civilizations to high temperatures, rather than to rocks.

These materials record the direction and magnitude of the geomagnetic field at the time and place at which they cooled down after being baked. The results of these investigations are shown in Figure 51, in which the measured values have been used to predict the strength of the field at the Earth's magnetic equator. This enables specimens from different latitudes to be compared. The *average* strength of the field appears to have undergone a cyclic variation with a period of around 10^4 years, a period similar to that for the variations in the dipole orientation.

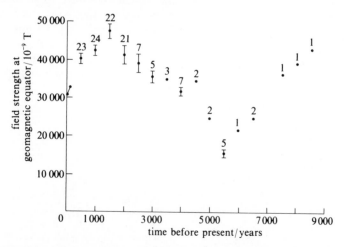

FIGURE 51   Change in the geomagnetic field strength at the geomagnetic equator for the past 8 000–9 000 years. The points are average values of all determinations within 500-year intervals. The number of determinations averaged is shown above each point and the error bars indicate uncertainties. The short sloping bar on the left is the line from Figure 49.

One final point: palaeomagnetic data show us that the Earth's dipole field has totally *reversed* its polarity many times in the past! The implications of this remarkable finding will become clear in Section 5; we mention it here simply to reinforce the point that the Earth's magnetic field is extremely variable with time.

3.4.3 IMPLICATIONS OF SECULAR VARIATION

Although the Earth's magnetic field is mainly dipolar, this does not mean that it is produced by a bar magnet but only that its shape is very much *like* that of a bar magnet. Clearly, both the time variations in the dipole field component, and the existence and rapid time variations in the non-dipole field component tell us that the field must have its origin in *dynamic processes* inside the Earth which operate on short time-scales (10–10^4 year variations have been described above). Whatever the composition of the Earth's interior, it is impossible that a permanent, solid magnet is responsible for the magnetic field because it could not change its characteristics at the rate observed. This leads us tentatively to suggest that the field must originate in a medium that can vary rapidly with time, such as a *fluid* medium (i.e. a gas or a liquid). This will be an important consideration in our discussion of models for the internal structure and composition of the Earth in Section 4.

There is another aspect of the Earth's interior which reinforces this conclusion about the dynamic origin for the magnetic field. As you saw in Section 1.3.1 the Earth's interior is, by everyday standards, extremely hot, producing huge volumes of volcanic material at temperatures well over $1\,000\,°C$ from depths of up to $100\,km$ or more. At greater depths, the interior of the Earth will be very much hotter than $1\,000\,°C$. What are the implications of this for the origin of the magnetic field? You can demonstrate this for yourself by carrying out the following experiment.

EXPERIMENT 3

THE EFFECT OF TEMPERATURE ON MAGNETISM

TIME

This experiment takes about 25 minutes.

NON-KIT ITEM

gas or electric cooker, *not* a microwave oven (a camping stove is also suitable)

KIT ITEMS
Part I

bar magnet
lighter flints
square aluminium sheet

METHOD

The lighter flints in the Kit are made from a weakly magnetic material. First check that your lighter flints are magnetic by picking a couple of them up with the magnet. Then place the aluminium sheet on a ring or burner on the cooker, and carefully put two of the magnetic flints on the sheet.

Warning 1   Take care not to burn yourself during this experiment.

Warning 2   Do NOT heat either of the bar magnets. (You will understand why when you have done the experiment!)

Heat the flints by turning the cooker full on and allow about half a minute in the case of a gas cooker, and two to three minutes for an electric cooker, for the flints to become hot. Now carefully try to pick up the flints again with the magnet, and note what happens.

Turn off the heat and *allow about 15 minutes* for both the aluminium sheet and the flints to cool.

Warning 3   The aluminium sheet may stay hot for longer than you expect. Leave it, if you are uncertain whether or not it is sufficiently cool to touch.

Now try to pick up the flints again, and note what happens.

ITQ 20   (a) What do you conclude about the magnetic behaviour of the flints when they were hot?

(b) What do you conclude about the magnetic behaviour of the flints after cooling?

The observations you have just made have important implications for the origin of the Earth's magnetic field. All magnetic materials behave in the same kind of way as the lighter flints when heated. The only difference is the actual temperature above which the material ceases to be a magnet; there is a characteristic temperature for each type of material. This temperature is known as the **Curie temperature**, named after Pierre Curie, who discovered the effect at the turn of the century. Although the Curie temperature is different for different magnetic materials, there is no material known that could be present inside the Earth with a Curie temperature greater than 1 200 °C. Because the temperature deep inside the Earth is much higher than this we must conclude that *it is impossible for the Earth's magnetic field to be produced simply by magnetic effects like those shown by bar magnets.* This reinforces the conclusions we made from observations of the rate at which the field changes, which is that the Earth's magnetic field cannot be produced by a permanent solid magnet at or near the centre of the Earth.

So we are left with a paradox: the Earth has a magnetic field, produced internally, where the temperatures are too hot for the material to be magnetic. How can this paradox be resolved? As you will see in Section 4, we need a mobile medium of a suitable composition, at a high temperature and incorporating a source of energy; within such a medium there *are* processes whereby a dynamically varying magnetic field can be produced. The field originates deep in the core of the Earth where a suitable medium is thought to exist.

This last aspect of the Earth's magnetic field will have to be taken into account along with all the seismic evidence when we construct our model of the Earth's interior. Accordingly, we shall start by considering the information which we have from seismological investigations, and then go on to incorporate the magnetic information.

Finally, you should note that the TV programme 'Magnetic Earth' illustrates various aspects of the Earth's dipole and non-dipole field components but is concerned primarily with rock magnetism, palaeomagnetism and the source of the Earth's magnetic field: a full synopsis of the programme appears in Section 5.

SUMMARY OF SECTION 3

1 The Earth's magnetic field can be thought of as the sum of two components, the dipole and non-dipole fields. The dipole field has essentially the same shape as it would have if a large bar magnet were located at the centre of the Earth. The non-dipole field is complex and irregular and accounts, on average, for about 5% of the total field strength.

2 The dipole field is geocentric, but, although the dipole axis is on average coincident with the Earth's axis of spin, the direction of the magnetic axis changes with time and currently is inclined to the rotation axis by about 11°.

3 Because the non-dipole field component is added to the dipole field, the total field is not quite that of a simple dipole. This is particularly evident on a field strength map. Moreover, it causes the positions of the dip poles (P_N and P_S in Figure 46), where the magnetic inclination is 90°, to be non-antipodal and to differ from the positions of the geomagnetic poles (M_N and M_S) of the dipole field at the Earth's surface.

4 The dipole component of the Earth's magnetic field is known through palaeomagnetic studies and direct observation to vary in strength and position (dipole wobble) periodically over about 10^4 years. In contrast, the non-dipole field component changes more rapidly, on a time-scale of 10–10^3 years.

5 Palaeomagnetic studies of the magnetism locked in ancient rocks make the simplifying assumption that the Earth's magnetic field has been that of a dipole. This assumption is valid if a large enough sample of rocks of a particular age is used to determine the ancient positions of the geomagnetic poles.

6 The secular variations (variations with time) of the magnetic field combined with the fact that any conceivable source materials within the Earth are well above their Curie temperatures suggests that the field must have a dynamic source, probably in a fluid medium rather than in a solid permanent magnet. Such a medium is believed to exist in the core of the Earth.

SAQ 13 Select from the following list (a)–(e) the two correct statements about bar magnets.

(a) The attractive magnetic force between two north poles of bar magnets decreases as the distance between them increases.

(b) The south poles of two bar magnets attract each other.

(c) A north pole and a south pole of two bar magnets attract each other.

(d) It is the south pole of a compass needle that points north.

(e) A bar magnet can pick up magnetic objects across a distance.

SAQ 14 Select from the following list (a)–(c) the one correct statement about dipolar magnetic fields.

(a) The direction of a dipolar field is parallel to the line connecting the two associated poles everywhere on the 'equatorial plane' of the field, i.e. on a plane through the centre of the field, perpendicular to the axis.

(b) The field lines of a dipolar field are everywhere parallel to the dipole axis.

(c) Anywhere in the magnetic field of a dipole, the north pole of a bar magnet is attracted in a straight line towards the south pole of the dipole.

SAQ 15 Describe in a few sentences for each:

(a) how the average strength of the Earth's magnetic field has changed with time over the last 9 000 years;

(b) how the orientation of the Earth's magnetic dipole axis appears to have changed over the last 7 000 years.

SAQ 16 What is meant by the non-dipole component of the Earth's magnetic field? Describe how the strength of the non-dipole component of the field varies with time.

SAQ 17 Which of the following statements are true and which are false? Explain your answers.

(a) An axial dipole is a dipole aligned along the Earth's axis of rotation.

(b) The geomagnetic dipole is axial at the present time.

(c) The geomagnetic poles in the Northern and Southern Hemispheres (M_N and M_S) are antipodal.

(d) At the geomagnetic pole in the Northern Hemisphere (M_N) the inclination of the Earth's magnetic field is $+90°$.

(e) The strength of the geomagnetic field produced by the Earth's dipole field component at the geomagnetic poles (M_N and M_S) is just over 60 000 nT.

(f) The north and south magnetic dip poles (P_N and P_S) are antipodal.

(g) The *north magnetic* pole of the (imaginary) magnetic dipole within the Earth is closer to the *north geographic* pole than to the *south geographic* pole.

SAQ 18 List three features of the Earth's magnetic field that suggest that it has a dynamic origin in the Earth's interior.

4 MODELLING THE EARTH'S INTERIOR

In this Section, we are concerned with bringing together all the observations we have made so far that bear on the structure and composition of the Earth's interior. We shall be drawing upon what you have learnt about: (a) the properties of different rocks (as summarized in your completed Table 1), (b) the density of the Earth and its variation with depth (discussed in Section 1.3), (c) the way in which seismic waves travel through the Earth (based on Section 2.5), and (d) the nature of the Earth's magnetic field (particularly Section 3.4).

We will start with the density of surface rocks. If you take the samples of granite (S1), gabbro (S5) and peridotite (S4) from the Kit and try to estimate their relative densities subjectively by how *heavy* they feel, you may be able to convince yourself that the gabbro is denser than the granite, and the peridotite is denser than the gabbro, as is in fact the case. The densities of the granite, the gabbro and the peridotite are about 2.7×10^3, 2.9×10^3 and $3.3 \times 10^3 \, \mathrm{kg \, m^{-3}}$, respectively. These are typical densities for surface rocks, and they contrast markedly with the average density for the whole Earth of $5.5 \times 10^3 \, \mathrm{kg \, m^{-3}}$ (see Section 1.3.3).

☐ What does this difference between the typical density of surface rocks and the Earth's average density imply about the density of the Earth's interior?

■ The below-average density of surface rocks implies that at least some of the rocks beneath the surface must have above-average densities.

You should recall from Section 1.3.3 that the pressure acting on rocks increases with depth because of the weight of the material above, so that rocks should become more dense with increasing depth inside the Earth. But there is another important factor: the deep interior of the Earth might be made of material with a totally different chemical composition from surface rocks, perhaps including rocks which are naturally more dense than typical surface rocks. The significance of these two factors which contribute to increases in density—increased pressure and change in chemical composition—will be a recurring theme throughout this Section.

The question now arises as to how these materials of increased density are distributed within the Earth. Recall the spherical avocado pear model of the Earth's structure described in Section 1.4: the outer 'skin' of the Earth is the crust, surrounding the 'flesh' or mantle and, at the centre, the 'stone' is the core. In this model, there are three concentric zones in which the density increases from the outer zone (the crust) towards the innermost zone (the core).

☐ How do we set about finding out the value of density at different depths?

■ You know from Section 2 that the speeds of seismic waves depend on density, so by observing their speeds we should be able to say something about density along different wave paths that penetrate to different depths (Figure 33).

Of course, we also know that the values of axial and rigidity moduli vary with depth according to the nature and state of compression of the materials present. To obtain values for density and elastic moduli at different depths is a complicated process. But we need to do this in order to decide what materials occur in the different layers. To simplify matters, we will start with the simplest possible seismic model of the Earth in which wave speeds (v_P and v_S) are constant throughout, even though we are well aware that this can be discounted on a straightforward consideration of density variations alone. We can then modify the model using actual observations of source–receiver travel times which we will convert into speeds.

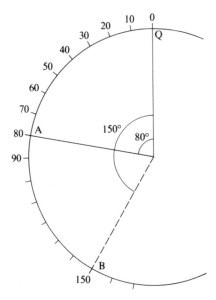

FIGURE 52 Distances between an earthquake with epicentre Q and recording stations A and B with epicentral angles of 80° and 150° respectively.

4.1 A SIMPLE SEISMIC MODEL

First, you need to note that seismologists do not speak of the distance between the epicentre of an earthquake and a seismic recording station in terms of kilometres but in terms of the angle which a radius from the epicentre to the Earth's centre makes with a corresponding radius from the recording station (Figure 52). This angle is termed the **epicentral angle**. Now we will take the seismic wave speeds of a typical surface rock (granite) and find out how typical these are for the Earth as a whole.

ITQ 21 Given that $v_P = 5.6\,\mathrm{km\,s^{-1}}$ and $v_S = 3.3\,\mathrm{km\,s^{-1}}$ (the values for granite which you calculated in SAQ 7), how long would it take for the first P-waves and S-waves from an earthquake to arrive at a recording station at an epicentral angle of 180°, i.e. on the opposite side of the Earth? Assume that the waves travel straight through the centre of the Earth, that the Earth is homogeneous and that the Earth's diameter is 12 740 km (6 370 km radius, from Section 1, multiplied by 2).

Now in our hypothetical model of a uniform Earth, there will be none of the refractions and reflections within the Earth which we discussed in Section 2.5, because there are no boundaries between layers with different seismic properties. Also, assuming a *uniform* Earth, we are implying that density does not increase with depth—in other words, that the effect of compression at depth can be ignored. This may seem rather artificial, but remember that we are beginning with the *simplest possible* model. Seismic waves will travel in straight lines, and the first arrival times at various points on the Earth's surface would simply be proportional to the shortest straight-line distance to the recording stations. We would obtain the results in Figure 53, which shows seismic waves radiating out uniformly from the earthquake.

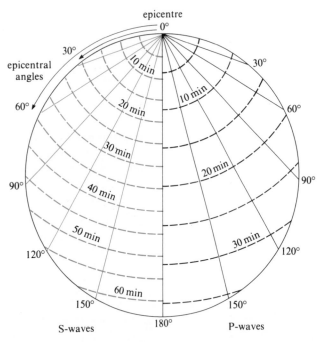

FIGURE 53 Section through a model according to which the Earth has uniform seismic properties identical to those of granite (SAQ 7). The curved lines show how far P-waves (black) and S-waves (red) will travel in a given number of minutes.

In Figure 54 (overleaf) the predicted travel times for a uniform Earth are shown dashed, with the actual times shown as solid curves. The lines are curved because we have plotted *epicentral angle* against time, rather than *linear distance* against time. For every 1° increase in epicentral angle, the linear distance increases by a relatively large amount near the epicentre, but

S-WAVE SHADOW ZONE

P-WAVE SHADOW ZONE

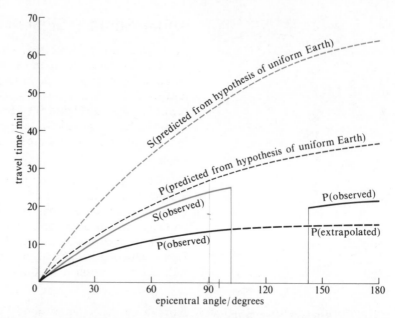

FIGURE 54   Travel-time curves for the first arrivals of P-waves (black) and S-waves (red) in the uniform Earth model of Figure 53 compared with the observations of actual times. The short dashed line does *not* represent real P-wave travel times; it is merely an extrapolation of the solid P-wave curve (from 0–103°) to allow comparison with the actual P-wave curve beyond 142°. (Epicentral angles of 103° and 142° are indicated by the two vertical lines.)

the increase in linear distance becomes less at greater epicentral angles (as you can see from Figure 52).

☐ Compare the travel times predicted from our uniform Earth hypothesis with those observed (Figure 54); what can you say about the speed of seismic waves through the real Earth as compared with the uniform Earth hypothesis? Concentrate on epicentral angles less than 103°.

■ The observed travel times are less than the corresponding predicted times; in other words, the waves are travelling *faster* than in the uniform Earth model.

The discrepancy between the predicted and observed travel times increases with increasing epicentral angle. In addition, there is a gap between epicentral angles of 103° and 142°, within which *no* waves are received at all. However, beyond 142°, although there are no S-waves, P-waves reappear, though they have *longer* travel times than would be expected simply from extrapolating the P-wave travel-time curve beyond 103° (short dashed curve in Figure 54).

There are obviously several ways in which reality differs from our simplest model, and we examine next how our simple model can be improved.

4.2 MODIFYING THE SIMPLE MODEL

It is quite a simple though time-consuming business to calculate travel-time curves based on observations of an earthquake whose epicentre and time are known from recordings of the arrivals of seismic waves made all over the Earth. Although Figure 53 shows one particular circular section through the spherical Earth, for a uniform Earth the travel times have the same pattern regardless of which section through the Earth's centre we draw, and regardless of the position of the focus. When plots of actual travel times are worked out, the same is true. It is the epicentral angle to the recording stations that determines when the seismic waves arrive, and not the geographic direction. Suppose, for example, that an earthquake which occurred in Japan was recorded in India at an epicentral angle of 50°, in southern Australia (80°) and in western Canada (90°). Although all these stations are in geographically different directions from Japan, the travel times observed would all plot on the same *observational* curves of travel times (Figure 54). Comparing such a set of observations with those from an earthquake at the North Pole, say, the same travel times would be recorded at stations at epicentral angles of 50° (e.g. in Madrid), as were found for India in the first earthquake. The travel times from the North Pole to Caracas (80°) would be the same as from Japan to southern Australia and, likewise, the travel times from the North Pole to Kampala (90°) would be the same as from Japan to western Canada. It is found that, wherever an earthquake occurs, the travel times for particular epicentral angles are always the same, and this observation leads us to a very important conclusion about the structure of the Earth's interior.

ITQ 22   All earthquakes are characterized by smooth travel-time curves (Figure 54) that are virtually identical, no matter where the earthquake takes place, and no matter how the recording stations are distributed. What does this tell you about the distribution of matter inside the Earth?
Hint: What would happen if the core in our avocado pear model were offset from the centre, for example?

So whatever variations of a property (or properties) of the Earth's interior causes the actual travel times to vary compared with those of our simplest uniform model, we can say that these variations are concentrically distributed. The spherical avocado pear model still seems to be a good approximation to the real Earth. Now we shall concentrate on the interpretation of Figure 54. You should notice the following features which are particularly important:

1   Both P-waves and S-waves arrive *earlier* than would be expected from the uniform model, and the time differences increase progressively with distance from the epicentre. This shows that both types of waves are travelling *faster* than they do in the rocks found at the surface of the Earth.

2   Beyond an epicentral angle of 103°, predictions from the uniform model and actual observations do not even remotely resemble each other. No traces of S-waves are recorded, and the range of epicentral angles greater than 103° is therefore known as the **S-wave shadow zone**. There is also a gap between epicentral angles of 103° and 142° at which no P-waves are received. This gap is known as the **P-wave shadow zone**.

3   At epicentral angles above 142°, P-waves take a lot longer than predicted by extending the 0–103° P-wave curve.

We shall defer consideration of the shadow zones to Section 4.4 and concentrate first on making deductions from the travel times up to epicentral angles of 103°. We know that density increases with depth inside the Earth. Could this be the cause of the faster travel times than predicted using the uniform model?

☐   What effect does increasing density have on seismic wave propagation speeds?

■   Since seismic wave speed = $\sqrt{\text{elastic modulus/density}}$ (see Equations 9 and 11), increasing density will lead to a decrease in seismic wave speed for a fixed elastic modulus.

As you will realize, this is exactly the opposite of what must happen—wave speeds appear to *increase* with depth. Therefore we must modify the model still further.

☐   If wave speeds and density are both to increase with depth, what must be happening to the elastic moduli ψ and μ?

SEISMIC DISCONTINUITY

■ Given this constraint, the only way of satisfying the equation for wave speed (above) is for the elastic moduli to increase *faster* than the density increases with depth in the Earth.

Just to make this absolutely clear, if the denominator on the right-hand side of the equation for wave speed increases, then the numerator must increase more rapidly if the whole expression on the right-hand side is to increase. In terms of the ball and spring model of Section 2, we can think of the balls and springs being squashed closer together at greater depth to give greater density, and at the same time, this makes the material less compressible and gives it greater rigidity, so that the elastic moduli also increase.

Let us now review the modifications which we have made to our model so far. For the part of the Earth through which the waves are passing to recording stations at epicentral angles up to 103°, we have a distinctly non-uniform Earth model in which:

---

1 Density increases with depth.

2 Elastic moduli increase with depth, at a faster rate than the density increases.

3 As a result of (1) and (2), both P- and S-wave speeds increase with depth.

4 Whatever changes in the Earth's interior cause these variations, they are arranged concentrically; that is to say, at any particular distance from the Earth's centre, the seismic properties have values that are characteristic of the distance from the centre.

The fact that seismic wave speeds vary has a consequence that we have not so far considered in this Section.

□ Obviously, variations in wave speed affect travel times, but what else happens if wave speeds change?

■ The velocity of the wave also changes (see Section 2.5); seismic waves are refracted (and/or reflected) when passing from one material into another in which they have a different speed of propagation.

So we should not expect the paths of the waves in our revised model of the Earth to be straight lines. So far, we have not established that there are any *distinct* boundaries across which there would be sharp changes in direction (as in Figure 27). However, we have built into our model a general increase in seismic wave speed with depth. To judge from the progressively widening gap between predicted and observed travel times in Figure 54, it appears that the wave speed increase may be *continuous*.

ITQ 23 What effect will a continuous change in wave speed have on a P-wave transmitted downwards from a point near the surface at an angle of, say, 25° to the horizontal? (Think back to our discussion of refraction in Section 2.5.)

Clearly the waves that reach epicentral angles up to 103° are passing through the *outer* parts of the Earth. If you think about arrivals at very small epicentral angles, the waves have not been able to penetrate deeply into the Earth (see Figure 34). The gradual and continuous increase in travel times up to epicentral angles of 103° supports the idea that wave speeds increase progressively for waves that penetrate deeper and deeper. But notice that the wave which arrives at 103° must have reached a depth in the Earth beneath which the paths of the waves are radically different. How can we work out the path of the wave which emerges at 103°, and so find the depth to which it penetrates?

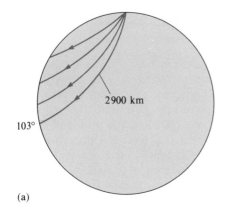

(a)

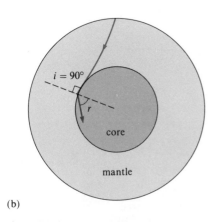

(b)

FIGURE 55 (a) A family of seismic waves continuously refracted through the Earth's mantle showing that the wave emerging at 103° penetrates to a maximum depth of 2900 km. (b) Waves reaching *just below* 2900 km strongly refracted into the lower-speed material of the core. Note that the wave shown in (b) is striking the core–mantle boundary at right angles so that the angle *r* is the critical angle of refraction (cf. critical angle of incidence in Figure 30).

To do this, we need to make one or two plausible assumptions about what the part of the Earth traversed by the waves arriving up to 103° *might* be made of, so that we can see how near our predictions then come to the observations we need to explain. You might be surprised to learn that rocks such as peridotite (specimen S4) have actually been brought up to the surface from depths of around 150 km or more (i.e. from within the mantle) by geological processes such as volcanic eruptions and large-scale faulting. So specimen S4 is a sample of part of the Earth's interior. It has been possible for several decades to perform laboratory experiments on rocks like this to investigate their properties under conditions which simulate these depths. Using powerful hydraulic presses, experimenters have created pressures equivalent to depths of several hundred kilometres. At the same time, by developing special container materials which have particularly high melting points, it has been possible to reproduce the high temperatures which occur at these upper mantle depths.

On the basis of these and other observations we believe that much of the Earth's mantle (the 'flesh' in the spherical avocado pear model) is made of peridotite. (We shall be dealing with the crust–mantle boundary later—remember from Section 1.4 that it lies within a few tens of kilometres of the surface.) Given that we have a peridotite mantle, using the known seismic properties of peridotite and making the necessary allowances for the effects of compression, we can calculate how seismic wave speeds will vary as waves are transmitted downwards into the peridotite mantle. These calculations of speeds allow wave paths to be predicted, and they take the form of the series of continuously refracted curves shown schematically in Figure 55a (which resembles Figure 34 but which also takes into account the wave path that emerges at 103°). In Figure 55a, there are no wave paths shown from the source to receiving stations at epicentral angles just greater than 103°, corresponding to observations (Figure 54).

This leads us to a very important result: *the waves recorded at 103° penetrate furthest into the mantle, reaching a depth of 2900 km*. At this depth, we can predict from the results of experiments on peridotite that the density will be about $5.4 \times 10^3 \, kg \, m^{-3}$—still slightly less than the Earth's average density. So there must be even denser material at greater depths, and if this material decreases the speed of P-waves there will be refraction *towards* the normal as shown in Figure 55b. This would explain (i) the P-wave shadow zone in Figure 54 and (ii) the rather greater travel times than expected from 0–103° data for deeply penetrating P-waves emerging between 142° and 180°. We shall consider this refraction in more detail later, but notice now that there is another important piece of evidence in Figure 54: no S-waves occur at epicentral angles greater than 103°.

☐ What does the absence of S-waves suggest about the nature of the material below 2900 km depth, corresponding to an epicentral angle of 103°.

■ Remember from Section 2.3 that S-waves can only be transmitted through materials that have a non-zero rigidity modulus. This means that the material below 2900 km depth must have a zero rigidity modulus—*it must be a liquid.*

The existence of a liquid layer below 2900 km satisfactorily explains why there is an S-wave shadow zone beyond 103°. The actual value of this depth is obtained using our observations of P- and S-wave travel times up to epicentral angles of 103° with the assumption that the material is peridotite. Thus we have a very distinct boundary or **seismic discontinuity** at this depth where strong refractions occur (Figure 55b). This is the most marked seismic discontinuity within the Earth, and corresponds also to a major compositional boundary, which is also a solid–liquid boundary, as we shall see shortly. This is the core–mantle boundary and, in effect, is the boundary between the flesh and the stone in our spherical avocado pear model of the Earth. Having defined this major boundary, we can now proceed to think further about the material which occurs on either side, starting with the mantle.

4.3 THE DETAILED STRUCTURE OF THE EARTH'S MANTLE

So far, we have been assuming that the mantle is *homogeneous* in composition (i.e. that its composition is the same throughout), with density and elastic moduli of the mantle material increasing with depth due to compression. As you might expect, the true picture is not quite that simple! Detailed studies of P-wave travel times have produced the profile of speed varying with depth shown in Figure 56. Notice that there is a zone from 400 km to 1 050 km depth across which the P-wave speed increases, with some distinct steps, from $8 \, \mathrm{km \, s^{-1}}$ to $11 \, \mathrm{km \, s^{-1}}$. This zone of change is known as the **transition zone** and its base separates the **upper mantle** from the **lower mantle**. But why is it transitional?

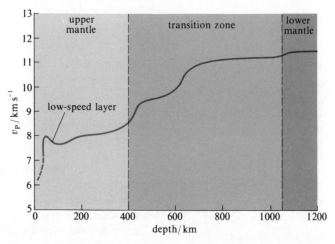

FIGURE 56   Graph of P-wave speed against depth in the upper 1 200 km of the Earth's mantle (continuous line). The dashed part of the line represents the speed in the outermost layer of the Earth (the crust), which is discussed in Section 4.5.

Experiments on peridotite have shown that under high pressures the internal structure of the rock changes so that the constituent particles become more compacted.

☐ What will be the result of this change on the density of the peridotite?

■ The density will increase.

It is thought that the three steps in the P-wave speed profile across the transition zone are due to stepwise jumps in the density of peridotite and, of course, in its axial modulus, *without any change in composition*. Such a change in structure is known as a **phase change**. A more familiar example of such structural differences is the contrast between diamonds, density $3.5 \times 10^3 \, \mathrm{kg \, m^{-3}}$, and graphite (pencil 'lead'), density $2 \times 10^3 \, \mathrm{kg \, m^{-3}}$. Diamond is a compressed form of graphite that is produced naturally at depths of nearly 200 km within the Earth's mantle, and then brought to the surface by volcanoes. If diamonds are subjected to very high temperatures at atmospheric pressure they can be changed into graphite. (We do *not* recommend this experiment!) The changes from ice to liquid water and from water to steam are also phase changes with no change in composition but these are also *changes of state* (from solid to liquid and from liquid to gas).

To summarize, the transition zone is characterized by three separate phase changes, all in the solid state, where axial modulus increases rapidly and density also increases. Nevertheless, we think that the lower mantle contains the same chemical ingredients as peridotite (principally silicates of iron and magnesium) and in the same proportions. There are no other phase or chemical changes in the lower mantle, in which v_P, ψ and ρ all increase steadily with depth due to increasing compression.

Look at Figure 56 again, and remember that here we are only considering the outermost 1 000 km or so of the Earth, which, you will remember, has an average radius of 6 370 km. The feature we have not yet discussed is the 'dip' in speed which is shown at about 100 km depth. In 1926, the seismologist Beno Gutenberg noted that seismic waves from earthquake foci at depths between 50 and 250 km took longer to arrive than they should have done on the assumption of a homogeneous upper mantle. He suggested that there was a layer between these depths which had a markedly lower P-wave speed than expected, and this came to be known as the *low-velocity layer* though, strictly, it is a **low-speed layer** (Figure 35). S-wave speeds are also considerably reduced in this layer and many of the waves originating in this layer are trapped as described in Section 2.5.

☐ Thinking back to our discussion of the core–mantle boundary, can you suggest a reason for the drop in wave speed in the low-speed layer? Remember that a drop in speed can result from a decrease in elastic modulus, or from a rise in density.

■ There must be a decrease in the values of the elastic moduli since we do not expect a change in composition—all the upper mantle zone is composed of peridotite.

So we need to find a mechanism by which elastic modulus can decrease while composition stays the same. Well, as we said earlier, P-wave speed is reduced and S-wave speed drops to zero in a liquid layer. However, S-wave speed is only *reduced* in the low-speed layer, rather than becoming zero.

☐ Now, what would happen to the axial and rigidity moduli if we have a partially molten (i.e. partly liquid) layer, rather like the slush which forms as snow begins to melt?

■ The values of elastic moduli will be *reduced* because the material will be more compressible and more susceptible to shear deformation.

To help you understand this phenomenon note that, in slush, most of the individual ice crystals are in contact with their neighbours, but there are also some gaps where the crystals have started to melt and these spaces are filled with water. It is because of these looser connections that the partially molten ice has less rigidity and is more compressible than the equivalent solid ice. Similarly, mantle peridotite becomes partially molten at depths where the temperature exceeds about 1 000 °C; here the values of elastic moduli and seismic wave speeds are reduced because of the presence of partially molten material.

As we noted in Section 1.3.1 (ITQ 2), temperatures of 1 000 °C are reached at about 50 km depth in the Earth and this accounts for the top of the low-speed layer (Figure 56). Beneath this depth, the *rate* of increase in temperature with depth gradually becomes less than is required to keep the mantle peridotite partially molten. So the low-speed layer continues down to only about 150–250 km depth, depending on location, and the remainder of the mantle is thought to be in the solid state. Incidentally, the low-speed layer is where the molten material forms that is eventually erupted in many volcanoes. The temperature does not rise high enough for all the components of peridotite to melt. In fact, only about 5% melt exists in the low-speed layer (the remainder is in the solid state), and it is the melt which has the composition of basalt. (Specimen S3 in the Kit is an example.)

ELECTRIC CURRENT

ELECTRICAL CONDUCTOR

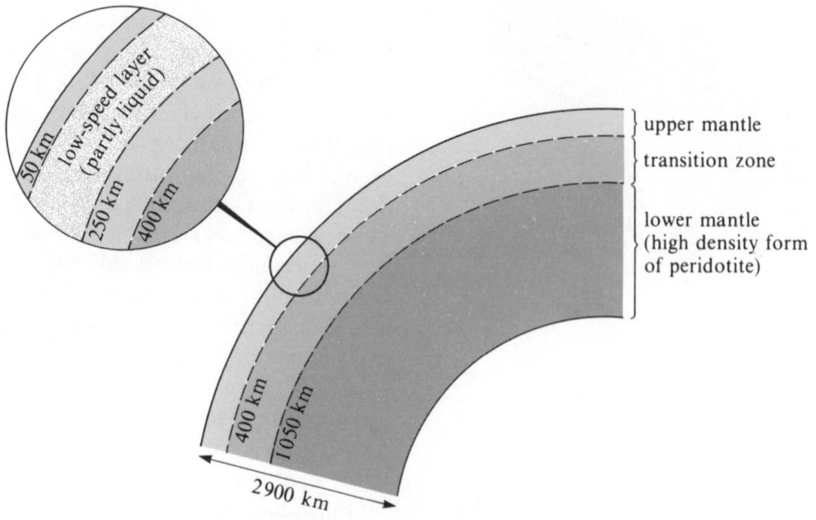

FIGURE 57 A summary of the structure and composition of the Earth's mantle.

The properties of the mantle are summarized below (and in Figure 57 above).

1   The mantle consists of three principal parts: the upper and lower mantle and a transition zone (400–1 050 km depth) at the base of the upper mantle.

2   The upper mantle is composed of peridotite but, within the transition zone, phase changes affect the material so that, although it still has the composition of peridotite, it has a different structure which is more compact than the peridotite with which you are familiar (specimen S4 in the Kit).

3   The lower mantle is composed entirely of the compact, high density form of peridotite, which reaches a density of $5.4 \times 10^3 \, \text{kg m}^{-3}$ at the base of the mantle (2 900 km depth).

4   Within the upper mantle, there is a seismic low-speed layer at depths of between 50 and 250 km within which up to 5% of the peridotite is partially molten. The melt has the composition of basalt (specimen S3 in the Kit) and it is thought that many of the basaltic magmas, erupted at volcanoes, form in the low-speed zone.

At this stage, you might reflect that we have produced a fairly elaborate model of the Earth's interior from depths of a few kilometres down to 2 900 km. This is just a brief summary of all that is known—which could occupy a whole Course Unit in its own right! Bear in mind that we have probed deep into the Earth without ever having seen a sample from depths greater than about 200 km. Whether our knowledge of the mantle has impressed you or not, the deductions we are about to make about the *even more* inaccessible core of the Earth are much more amazing, given that they are all based on 'remotely sensed' data.

4.4 THE NATURE OF THE EARTH'S CORE

We now reach the central part of our spherical avocado pear model of the Earth: the core. In many ways this is the most interesting and exciting region of the Earth to discuss and it turns out that, once again, Earth scientists have surprisingly detailed knowledge about the nature of the core—much of which, though, is beyond the scope of this Course. However, we can familiarize you with most of the important features of the core by bringing together several strands of evidence which we have already introduced.

ITQ 24   Summarize what you know already about the core from:

(a) S- and P-wave arrivals beyond epicentral angles of 103°;

(b) the average density of the Earth and of the mantle;

(c) the combination of (a) and (b) (think about axial modulus);

(d) magnetic data, given that the Earth's magnetic field originates in the core.

(*Note:* It is important that you attempt this 'revision' ITQ and then check your answer against the answer at the back before proceeding).

In this Section we shall be examining some of the implications of magnetic data for the nature of the core (ITQ 24d) before going on to extend our inferences in ITQ 24a–c by looking at seismic data on the core in a little more detail. We shall need to ask why it is that P-waves emerge at 142° and what the implications of travel times are for the exact values of axial modulus and density in the core. Notice that the suggestion that axial modulus decreases from the mantle to the outer part of the core is consistent with the liquid nature of the outer core. In general (as you know from Section 2.4), axial modulus values increase with increasing resistance to compression, so they will be much lower for liquids than solids. In fact, *it is the combined effect of a decrease in axial modulus and an increase in density that causes the large drop in P-wave speed across the core–mantle boundary.* We return to this in Section 4.4.2.

4.4.1 THE SOURCE OF THE EARTH'S MAGNETIC FIELD

In answering part (d) of ITQ 24 you may have felt that the Earth's magnetism tells us very little about the *nature* of the core, other than that it is liquid (which we know already from seismic data) and that it is in a dynamic state. Shortly, however, you will see that there are several conclusions (suggested by the magnetic properties of the Earth) about the composition of the core which can help us to make sense of the seismic information. This is an example of the way in which the development of concepts and models like those we are discussing has involved interaction between scientists in many disciplines, and advances in one discipline often occur before other disciplines are 'ready' to use the information. One consequence of the sometimes haphazard way in which models of major phenomena are developed is that the 'finished product' usually appears much more coherent than it did during construction (as is the case with any major building project!).

In order to understand the possible mechanism for producing the Earth's magnetic field in the liquid core we need to consider some aspects of *electromagnetism*—the inextricable linking of electrical and magnetic phenomena—beyond the basic properties of magnets and their fields which we considered in Section 3.2.

First you need to have some idea of what electricity is. The idea that a battery has a positive and a negative terminal will be familiar to you. Both terminals need to be connected to an electrical gadget to make it work; if there is a break in any of the connecting wires, nothing happens. Thus it seems quite reasonable to think of electricity as something that *flows* from one terminal of the battery to the other. This of course begs the question: What kind of thing can flow along a piece of metal wire? It will be sufficient for your understanding of Earth magnetism if you can accept for the moment that an **electric current** is due to the flow of tiny particles called *electrons* along an **electrical conductor**, for example, the wire. (You will learn a lot more about electrons in Units 11–12.) Now when electrons flow to make an electric current, they create a magnetic field around the conductor through which they are flowing, as shown in Figure 58. Conversely, the motion of an electrical conductor in a magnetic field will generate an electrical current.

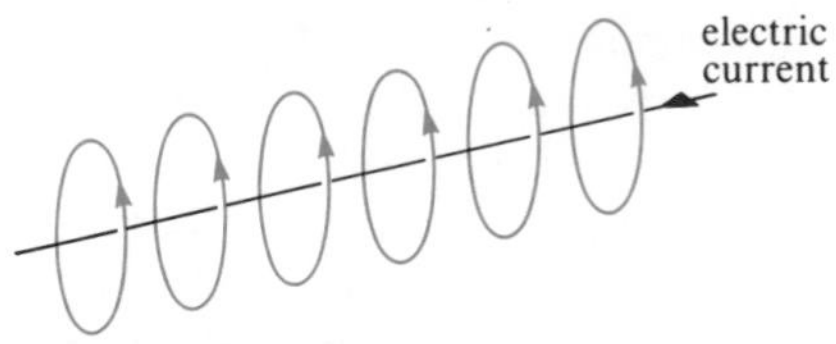

electric current

FIGURE 58 The magnetic field around a wire carrying an electric current from right to left.

□ Suggest how the phenomenon of electromagnetism might provide an explanation for the origin of the Earth's magnetic field.

■ If the liquid core is an electrical conductor in which electrical currents are flowing then we would expect a magnetic field to be produced.

Such a field could easily change rapidly as the liquid moves, and so could account even for the rapid rates of change of the non-dipole field component. The exact details of how electric currents within the liquid core produce an essentially dipolar field are not well understood. But we do know, as demonstrated in the TV programme 'Magnetic Earth', that when electricity passes through a helical coil of wire known as a **solenoid** (Figure 59) the resulting magnetic field is dipolar. The key feature to notice is that *the magnetic field produced by a solenoid is identical in form to that produced by a bar magnet of the same size* (see Figure 40).

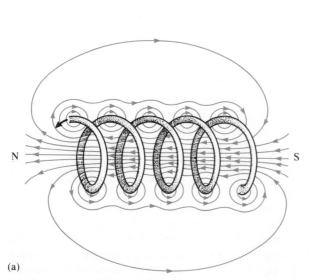

(a)

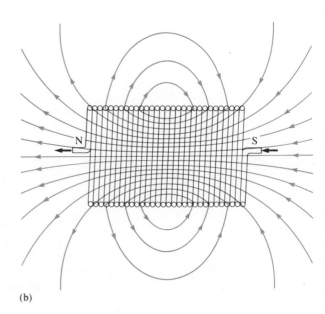

(b)

FIGURE 59 (a) The magnetic field produced by a loosely wound coil of wire (solenoid) carrying an electric current from right to left; (b) the magnetic field produced by a tightly wound solenoid, with the positions of magnetic north and south marked N and S. The black arrows denote electric current.

So now we are really beginning to understand something about origin of the Earth's magnetic field. We need electrical **current loops** of the kind shown in Figure 59 within the liquid core and this implies that the core must conduct electricity. The most generally accepted model of this phenomenon was first suggested by the physicist Joseph Larmor in 1919, and this has been elaborated by various geophysicists, notably Edward Bullard at Cambridge, since 1950. In this model, a *series* of electric currents (Figure 60) flow within the conducting material, each with the current flowing in the helical pattern of a solenoid. The individual magnetic fields produced by these separate current loops add up to produce the total dipole magnetic field.

The arrangement in Figure 60 has several attributes which make it plausible as a mechanism for producing the Earth's field. First, the core is rotating with the Earth and this may constrain the helical current loops to form with their axes approximately parallel to the axis of rotation. This would explain why, on average, the dipole field is aligned with the rotational axis, with minor fluctuations in the direction and relative strengths of the current loops causing the dipole wobble. Secondly, small current loops which are not aligned with the rest may be responsible for the non-dipole field component. Thirdly, westerly drift of this component (Figure 48) may simply be the result of the liquid core rotating slightly more slowly than the mantle because there is no rigid attachment between the two.

Despite the apparent plausibility of the model shown in Figure 60 there are numerous competing refinements which are being debated today. However, all agree that the magnetic field is due to electric currents in the conducting core and the problem then is to account for the existence of those currents. We hinted at this earlier when discussing the nature of electromagnetism.

☐ Suppose that an electrically conducting liquid in the outer core were moving in some way. What would happen if there were a magnetic field present?

■ Electric currents would flow in the moving conductor.

FIGURE 60 A possible arrangement
of helical electric current loops within
the liquid core that could produce the
Earth's dipolar magnetic field.

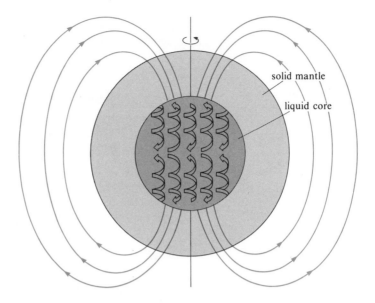

solid mantle

liquid core

However, the presence of an electric current in a moving conductor would itself produce a moving magnetic field, which would create new currents in the conducting material. Lest you should think that this sounds a bit like the fabled, and impossible, perpetual motion machine which goes on and on without any external driving force, we should remind you that the production of both electric currents and magnetic fields is a result of the *movement of the conductor*, which does require a driving force of some sort. An adaptation of Larmor's model which takes this into account is known as the **self-exciting dynamo**, because the field causes (i.e. 'excites') the current and the current then produces a field, and so on. The logic is set out in the flow chart of Figure 61a and a mechanical analogue of the type illustrated in the TV programme 'Magnetic Earth' appears in Figure 61b. In the analogue, a solenoid producing a magnetic field (red arrows) is located beneath a rotating copper disc, the conductor, mounted on an axle which rotates. There are sliding contacts (brushes) on the disc and axle. Because the disc rotates in a magnetic field an electric current (black arrows) flows. As it flows through the solenoid it maintains the magnetic field, which produces (self-excites) more current, and so on, provided that the axle continues to rotate. The only problem, identified in Figure 61a, is that an initial magnetic field *or* electric current is required to start the self-exciting dynamo working. We believe the most likely candidate for the Earth is that a magnetic field originating in the Sun early in the Earth's history was responsible for 'starting up' the Earth's self-exciting dynamo mechanism in the core.

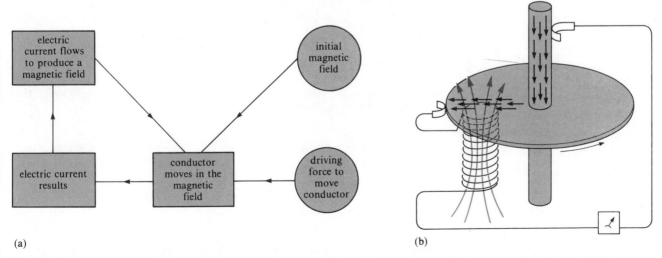

(a)

(b)

FIGURE 61   (a) Flow chart of the sequence of events and effects involved in the self-exciting dynamo. (Note that an initial magnetic field—as shown here—or an electric current is required to 'start' the dynamo action.) (b) A mechanical analogue model of the self-exciting dynamo. Magnetic field lines are shown in red, the electric current in black. (Details are given in the text.)

We can summarize our model for the mechanism by which the Earth's magnetic field is produced as follows:

1   The liquid core is composed of a conducting material in which electric currents can flow, thereby inducing a magnetic field.

2   The patterns in which the electric currents flow are such that an essentially dipolar field results. The currents are probably flowing in a series of helical loops like giant solenoids oriented roughly parallel to the Earth's axis of rotation.

3   Because the field has a dynamic source, the features of the non-dipole component of the Earth's field can be accounted for by relatively small perturbations in the pattern of the electric currents.

4   It is probable that the field is maintained by a self-exciting dynamo mechanism, in which electric currents are produced as the conducting material of the liquid part of the core moves through a magnetic field, and the electric currents thus produced themselves induce a magnetic field.

This leaves just one question: What is the source of energy, the driving force, which causes the conducting liquid of the core to move (Figure 61a)? As you can see from the analogue model in Figure 61b, if the motion of the conductor stops, the field and current are lost. Unfortunately, a full discussion of this question is outside the scope of this Course; suffice it to say that the part of the core generating the field is being stirred by a process known as *convection* in which dense material sinks and light material rises continuously. The exact cause of this convection is not known with any certainty and is much debated. As we leave our discussion of the origin of the Earth's magnetic field, the key point to stress is point (1) above—that the material of which the liquid core is made *must be capable of conducting electric currents*. Having said that, it will probably come as no great surprise to you to learn that we think the core is predominantly made of *metallic iron*, which is one of the best conductors known, and we shall elaborate on this in the remainder of Section 4.

4.4.2 THE STRUCTURE OF THE CORE

At this stage, we must return to seismic evidence and think about what happens when P-waves enter the iron-rich liquid core. If you look back to Figure 55b for a moment, you will see that we showed there a rather special P-wave, one that just grazes the core and is strongly refracted. The angle of incidence i is 90°, so this makes r a critical angle, in fact the *critical angle of refraction*. (This is the reverse of the situation in Figure 30, where the wave was travelling from the lower-speed into the higher-speed medium at the *critical angle of incidence*, and was refracted at an angle of 90° to the normal.) In the case of the core–mantle boundary, waves travelling into the core meet a lower-speed medium. Now the critical angle of refraction at this boundary has been estimated by seismologists to be 36.6°, so a *critical P-wave* will be bent by $(90-36.6)° = 53.4°$ on entering the core. Perhaps it is not surprising that the density of the iron-rich core is more than twice that of the peridotite mantle!

ITQ 25   (a) Given that the speed of P-waves at the base of the mantle is known to be $13.6 \, \text{km s}^{-1}$, what will be their speed in the outermost part of the core?

(b) By how much will a P-wave be bent if it strikes the core at a steeper angle of incidence, say at 42°?

So you can see that seismic waves are bent by progressively smaller amounts as angles of incidence become smaller and, of course, a wave that strikes the boundary at right angles (zero angle of incidence) will continue undeviated. The three wave paths we have just been discussing are shown in

Figure 62 which you should now study carefully—note that we have rounded off the values of the angles to the nearest whole degree.

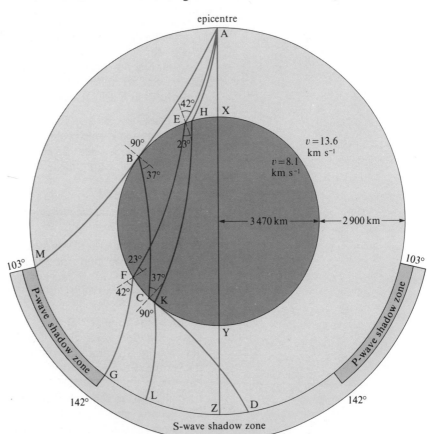

FIGURE 62 P-wave refractions at the core–mantle boundary showing the origin of the P-wave shadow zone.

☐ Why do you think we have shown *curved* wave paths in the core?

■ The reasoning is analogous to that applied for seismic waves in the mantle (Figure 55a)—the P-waves must be undergoing continuous refraction as their speed of propagation increases.

In turn, this means that our iron-rich liquid must be becoming less compressible (and probably more dense), i.e. its axial modulus must be increasing as the pressure increases.

☐ Now what happens to P-waves as they emerge from the core back into the mantle? How much are they bent?

■ You should be able to see that they are refracted back by the same angle as when they entered the core, and this is because we are dealing with the same speed difference.

This means that the critical P-wave which grazes the core–mantle boundary at B in Figure 62 emerges at C and, after being bent strongly at both B and C, finally reaches the surface at D on the opposite side of the Earth to that in which it first started being propagated (path AB). All waves meeting the core–mantle boundary between B and E (where the angle of incidence is 42°) travel similar paths and reach the surface between D and G. As the point of contact with the core–mantle boundary varies from B to E, the point of emergence at the surface moves from D to G. Consequently, you might expect that a wave meeting the boundary between E and H at an angle of incidence of less than 42° would emerge from the core between F and B and thus reach the surface between G and M.

☐ But this does not occur. Why?

73

■ The reason is that waves are now striking the core quite close to the vertical and so are not strongly refracted.

So path AEFG is also critical in some respects and it marks the limit of the P-wave shadow zone in that no P-waves refracted into the core can emerge at the surface at epicentral angles less than 142°. All waves striking the core–mantle boundary at incident angles less than 42° (between E and X in Figure 62) are refracted along paths such as AHKL to emerge from the core between F and Y, reaching the surface between G and Z.

Now comes the most recent and spectacular discovery of all. The first sign of this was some unexpected P-wave arrivals at epicentral angles near 180° which had taken about 25 seconds *less* to reach the receiver than predicted on the basis of a homogeneous core in which v_P increases due to compression.

☐ What can be deduced from this about P-wave speeds close to the centre of the Earth?

■ They must increase compared with predicted speeds in a homogeneous core. (Notice that these unexpected waves occur only at epicentral angles near 180° so, according to Figure 62, they should be waves that have passed very close to the centre of the Earth.)

At the same time (1972) a set of *reflected* arrivals was detected within the P-wave shadow zone which could best be explained as having been strongly deviated by a seismic discontinuity at 5 155 km depth, only 1 215 km from the centre of the Earth. Both of these 'new' wave paths are shown in Figure 63; the strongly deviated, reflected wave is ANPQR. The wave AXYZ travels 2 430 km through this newly defined zone, the **inner core** and arrives 25 seconds early. At the P-wave speed just above the discontinuity (10.1 km s^{-1}) the wave would take 241 seconds whereas it actually takes 216 seconds giving an inner core P-wave speed of 11.2 km s^{-1}. Wave ASTUVW

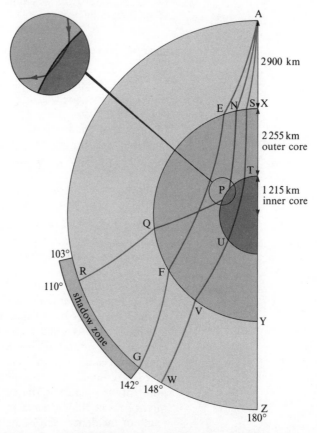

FIGURE 63 Earthquake wave refractions caused by the inner core. An outer core wave (AEFG) as in Figure 62 is shown for reference. The insert shows an enlargement of the path of the critically refracted (reflected) wave at P.

is similarly advanced in time and is refracted twice more (at T and U) than AHKL in Figure 62. These discoveries confirmed a long-held theory that the Earth has an inner core which is *solid* and which has a different composition from the surrounding liquid region, now defined as the **outer core**.

Another very significant discovery has been that part of the P-wave energy striking the inner core is used to generate S-waves which cross the inner core to regenerate P-waves again as they re-emerge into the liquid outer core. These P–S–P core waves take nearly 200 seconds longer to cross the inner core than simple P-waves alone: they have been detected in the myriad of arrivals close to the 180° epicentral angle, so again testifying to the solid nature of the inner core.

Finally, what about density? To cut a long story short, it turns out from seismic data and considerations of the Earth's average density, that the liquid outer core must have a density that increases due to compression from about $9.9 \times 10^3 \, \text{kg m}^{-3}$ at the core–mantle boundary to $12.3 \times 10^3 \, \text{kg m}^{-3}$ at the inner core–outer core boundary. The solid inner core has a density of about $13.5 \times 10^3 \, \text{kg m}^{-3}$ at the inner core–outer core boundary.

4.4.3 THE COMPOSITION OF THE CORE

You will recall that it is difficult to conduct laboratory experiments to simulate mantle conditions. The problem is even worse for the core where pressures over a million times that of the Earth's atmosphere are required to investigate core materials in the laboratory. Recent developments have produced a breakthrough so that experimenters can now place materials under appropriate conditions of pressure and temperature, but only for a short time. Samples are subjected to a predetermined explosive charge which causes a pressure wave, a P-wave, to pass through them. Electronic sensors are used to measure the effects of the pressure wave, and from these readings the density of the material and the speed of the shock wave can be worked out, and hence the axial modulus calculated. The results of these experiments have enabled us to make some quite reasonable predictions about the nature of the materials of the core.

First the experimenters had to decide what the likely composition of the core might be. The constraints were that the material must be electrically conducting *and* be abundant generally in the planets of the Solar System. The core amounts to about 16% of the Earth by volume and 31% by mass, and the only conducting material of sufficient abundance with the right kind of density is, as you know, metallic iron. Further support for the iron-rich core model was derived from a study of *meteorites* which are pieces of disrupted Earth-like planetary material that originate in the asteroid belt between the Sun-centred orbits of Mars and Jupiter. An important group is composed of a mixture of two metals, iron and nickel, mainly the former, and these **iron meteorites** are thought to represent core material from broken-up planets. You will learn more about these in Units 28–29.

Adding these pieces of evidence together, could the Earth's core be made of iron and perhaps some nickel? (Pure iron would have slightly too low a density, even at the extreme pressures estimated for the inner core.) Nickel is a little *more dense* than iron in both solid and liquid forms and it turns out that a good match to the inner core density deduced from seismic data—$13.5 \times 10^3 \, \text{kg m}^{-3}$—is obtained with a mixture of about *20% nickel with 80% iron*. But for the outer core, matters are not quite that simple.

ITQ 26 Experiments show that, at a compressional state equivalent to that of the outer core, just below its boundary with the mantle, pure liquid iron has a density of around $10.6 \times 10^3 \, \text{kg m}^{-3}$. On this basis, must the outer core be made of iron, iron and nickel or iron and something else?

On grounds of chemical abundances within the Solar System as well as from density considerations, it is thought that the yellowish material

Terms in AV sequence:

PLUTONIC

GABBRO

PILLOW LAVAS

PUMICE

RHYOLITE

sulphur is combined with iron in the outer core to form an *iron–sulphur mixture* in the approximate proportions 88% iron to 12% sulphur. (The chemical compound iron sulphide—which contains considerably more than 12% sulphur—is found at the Earth's surface in ore deposits where it is a yellowish looking mineral, often called 'fool's gold' and known as *pyrite* to the geologist.) A liquid iron–sulphur mixture is an ideal medium in which to generate the Earth's magnetic field by the self-exciting dynamo action. So we have a consistent solution to the question of the outer core composition which fits all the available evidence. Moreover, under the conditions of temperature and pressure which exist within the core, iron–sulphur mixtures are expected to be liquid whereas iron–nickel mixtures will be solid.

4.4.4 THE EARTH'S CORE: A SUMMING UP

In the preceding discussion, we have dealt with deducing the composition of the Earth's core at a fairly basic level, but we hope we have given you enough of the evidence for you to find the arguments convincing. We can now summarize our knowledge of the Earth's core as follows:

1   The magnetic field of the Earth originates in the liquid part of the core, and is likely to be induced by circulating electric currents in a conducting material. Evidence from meteorites, the abundances of chemical elements in the Solar System, and experimental data strongly suggest that the core is iron-rich.

2   P-wave speeds range from 8.1 to $10.1\,\mathrm{km\,s^{-1}}$ from the top to the bottom of the outer core, and range from 11.2 to $11.3\,\mathrm{km\,s^{-1}}$ in the inner core. This would be expected for layers which are both homogeneous in composition but in which axial modulus and density increase with depth as a result of compression.

3   The Earth has an inner core of radius $1\,215\,\mathrm{km}$ which is solid and is thought to consist of an 80% iron: 20% nickel mixture with a density of around $13.5 \times 10^3\,\mathrm{kg\,m^{-3}}$ at the inner core–outer core boundary.

4   The Earth's outer core extends from a depth of $2\,900\,\mathrm{km}$ down to the top of the inner core, and is liquid. It is thought to be composed of a mixture of 88% iron and 12% sulphur, with a density ranging from 9.9×10^3 to $12.3 \times 10^3\,\mathrm{kg\,m^{-3}}$.

The 'stone' of the spherical avocado pear model of the Earth really is a bit more complex than you might have imagined! In the final part of Section 4 we shall look at the 'skin' of the model—the Earth's crust, the thin outer layer on which we live, and the only layer which we can sample to any significant extent.

4.5 THE EARTH'S CRUST

As you began to discover from your study in Section 1 of the rock samples in the Kit, the Earth's crust is made up of a wide variety of materials. These are of particular interest, not simply because they determine the landscape in which we live, but also because they are the source, either directly or indirectly, of most raw materials used by the human race. Obvious examples are sand and gravel for the construction industries, coal and oil for the chemical and energy industries, gold and silver and a host of other rare materials for a variety of uses. Less obviously, the soils on which we grow our food are derived from the underlying rocks by the action of the weather.

4.5.1 IGNEOUS ROCK FORMATION (AV SEQUENCE)

This second AV sequence will show you in more detail the surprising amount of information which can be gained from just a single rock sample. The rocks in the Kit are just a limited selection of the major rock types of the Earth's crust, chosen to illustrate the range of environments and processes involved in their formation. You will see a much larger variety at Summer School but we hope that, before then, you will start to apply your new knowledge from these Units, to appreciate more about the countryside and about constructional and ornamental natural materials. You should now find the rock hand specimens and hand lens from your Kit. You will find the AV sequence on Tape 1 (Side 2, Band 2). Work through this AV sequence, filling in the blanks in Tables 5 and 6 as you go along.

TABLE 5   Characteristics of specimen S5 (for use with AV sequence)

Specimen	Description	Formation
S5	Texture *Crystal*	*Intrusive Igneous*
	Grain size *coarse*	....
Plate	....	....

TABLE 6   Formation of igneous rock types (for use with AV sequence)

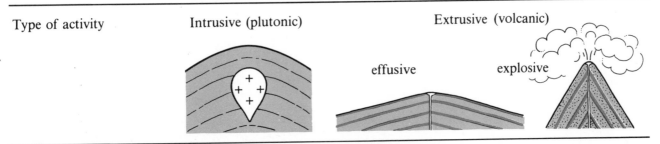

Type of activity	Intrusive (plutonic)	Extrusive (volcanic)	
		effusive	explosive

Rate of cooling

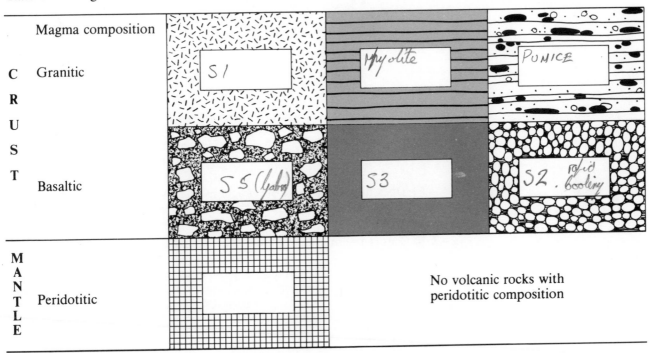

	Magma composition			
C R U S T	Granitic	S1	*Rhyolite*	PUMICE
	Basaltic	SS (gabbro)	S3	S2. *rapid cooling*
M A N T L E	Peridotitic		No volcanic rocks with peridotitic composition	

4.5.2 CRUSTAL STRUCTURE

The variety of all the Earth materials leads us to wonder about the relationship between the varied surface rocks and the peridotite mantle. In Units 7–8, you will be introduced to some of the *processes* by which the rocks of the crust have been formed, and in Unit 27 you will learn in more detail about how all crustal rocks have mantle peridotite as their ultimate original source, and about the complex processes which have nevertheless produced such a wide variety of end-products.

MOHOROVIČIĆ
DISCONTINUITY (MOHO)

OCEANIC CRUST

CONTINENTAL CRUST

Although we have left consideration of the relationship between the crust and the mantle to the last part of Section 4, the investigation of the relationship dates from the early 20th century. A Yugoslavian geologist, Andrija Mohorovičić (pronounced 'mo-horovichick'), studied seismograms for shallow-focus (less than 40 km deep) continental earthquakes recorded over distances up to 800 km from their epicentres. The surprising results showed that one set of P-wave and S-wave arrivals was followed soon after by another distinct set.

☐ How do you think this could happen? Think again about refractions within the Earth.

■ Mohorovičić deduced that there must be two distinct paths involved: one set of waves travelled *directly*, but the second set must have been *refracted* strongly after they had started moving downwards into the Earth.

Mohorovičić's idea is illustrated in Figure 64. One set, the 'direct' set of waves passes through an upper region of fairly uniform, low wave speed. The other set travels steeply downwards, is strongly refracted away from the normal at a boundary with higher-speed material and, after travelling through this material for much of the distance, it re-emerges to be refracted towards the normal and thence up to the receiver at the surface.

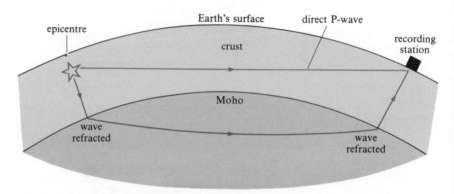

FIGURE 64   The Mohorovičić discontinuity (Moho). The Figure shows how both a direct P-wave and a P-wave refracted at the Moho will be recorded at distances up to several hundred kilometres.

☐ Does this remind you of refractions anywhere else in the Earth? What do we call this sort of boundary between two media with different wave speeds?

■ This is a seismic discontinuity, just like the core–mantle boundary.

This particular discontinuity is present around most of the Earth and separates the crust, where v_P is between 6 and 7 km s^{-1} from the mantle, where v_P starts at 8 km s^{-1} (Figure 64). This boundary is known as the **Mohorovičić discontinuity**, or **Moho** for short. It varies in depth between 5 and 11 km beneath the ocean floor but has an average depth of 35 km beneath continents, and is nearly 100 km deep beneath high mountain ranges (Figure 65). The reasons for these variations will be discussed at some length in Units 7–8, and in Unit 27. The crust is defined as the layer of the Earth above the Moho, and there are important differences between **oceanic crust** which floors all the great ocean basins, and the **continental crust** beneath the continents and the adjoining continental shelves at the edges of the oceans.

Although Mohorovičić discovered the discontinuity by studying natural earthquakes, seismologists have since learned much more about crustal structure using experimental explosions. Not only have the standard techniques of *seismic refraction* (described in Section 2) been employed, but a

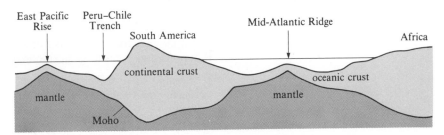

FIGURE 65 Schematic illustration of the oceanic and continental crust showing the variations in thickness in an east–west cross-section from the Pacific Ocean to Africa.

great deal has been learnt, particularly about the structure of oil- and coal-bearing regions, using *seismic reflection* methods (Section 6).

One of the results of the seismic investigation of oceanic crust has been to show that all the deep ocean basins of the Earth are floored by rocks which, beneath a thin veneer of sedimentary rocks, are all very similar. Remember that the gabbro and basalt samples in the Kit have the same chemical composition despite their quite dissimilar appearances—they differ only in grain size. Investigations of oceanic crust over the last 50 years, and particularly since it became possible to drill into the sea-bed in water depths of several kilometres, have revealed that this crust is everywhere of basaltic/gabbroic composition.

The oceanic crust is very thin compared to the continental crust (Figure 65) and also has a more homogeneous composition. The very wide range of continental rocks has exercised the minds of geologists ever since the pioneering work of William Smith and his contemporaries in the late 18th century. Many of the lowland areas of the continents (e.g. south-east Britain) are geologically young and expose sedimentary rocks at the surface. These overlie older, more compacted sedimentary rocks together with igneous and metamorphic rocks. Where these older and harder rocks are exposed at the surface, their resistance to weathering and erosion by rain and snow results in mountainous landscapes such as those of northern Scotland. The dominant rocks in these areas are intrusive granites, like the granite specimen in your Kit, together with a wide variety of metamorphic rocks. These rocks are actually typical of the deeper parts of the continental crust, but in Scotland geological processes have caused uplift of this crust and erosion has subsequently revealed these deeper rocks for our inspection.

So the geological investigation of older uplifted parts of the continental crust which have been eroded, together with seismic investigations and many other techniques, have enabled us to arrive at a quite detailed picture of the nature of the continental crust. The whole crust has an *average* composition which is quite close to that of granite, and which is markedly different from the basaltic/gabbroic composition of the oceanic crust.

This concludes our investigation of the Earth's internal structure and composition and we hope that you have gained some insight into the process whereby a scientific model is developed and refined. We started with the simplest possible model, that of a homogeneous Earth, and introduced refinements, step by step, to account for the results of observation and experiment. We have ended up with a quite complicated model, but we must emphasize that this is only a model, providing the best explanation for the data so far.

The development of this model has taken many years and has involved scientists of several different disciplines. On the way, many different models have been proposed and rejected, or partially accepted and incorporated into the present generally accepted picture. This process is still continuing, and the model is always open to refinement. It is always possible that some more evidence may come to light which will necessitate revision of our model—though we hope these revisions will be minor.

SUMMARY OF SECTION 4

The main conclusions of this important Section are summarized in Table 7, Figure 66 and the following statements.

1   Seismic wave travel times enable us to deduce physical properties such as density, and axial and rigidity moduli, deep inside the Earth.

2   The Earth has an iron-rich core which is liquid in its outer part and probably contains some sulphur; its inner part is solid and probably contains some nickel together with iron.

3   The Earth's magnetic field has its origin in electrical currents flowing in the outer core, and according to one model the field may be produced by a self-exciting dynamo mechanism.

4   The Earth has a peridotite mantle which has a transition zone separating its upper and lower parts, and a partially molten low-speed layer at comparatively shallow depths in the upper mantle.

5   The outer layer of the Earth, known as the crust, is the least dense part and is separated from the upper mantle by the Mohorovičić discontinuity.

6   The crust can be divided into two distinct types, of very different composition and thickness, namely the thin oceanic crust with a basaltic/gabbroic composition, and the thicker continental crust with a composition close to that of granite.

SAQ 19   Select the reasons from (a)–(d) below which correctly explain why we believe the mantle to be made of peridotite; briefly explain your answers.

(a) Peridotite has values of axial and rigidity modulus, and of density that are consistent with the wave speeds that are observed seismically.

(b) Several boreholes have penetrated to the mantle and have found peridotite.

(c) Peridotite is exposed in several places where the mantle reaches the surface of the Earth.

(d) Fragments of peridotite have been found in volcanic rocks which have been erupted from great depths.

SAQ 20   Explain in two or three sentences why we believe that the properties of the Earth's interior that determine seismic wave speeds are radially symmetric (i.e. the same at every point at a given distance from the centre of the Earth).

SAQ 21   (a) Are the major variations in seismic wave speed in the mantle caused by changes in composition or by phase changes of the mantle material?

(b) Which parts of the mantle are affected by the variations?

SAQ 22   Explain in a few sentences the main reasons for the existence of the Earth's P-wave shadow zone for arrivals of seismic waves at epicentral angles between 103° and 142°.

SAQ 23   Select from (a)–(f) below the two correct statements about seismic waves that pass down to meet the core–mantle boundary. Explain your choice.

(a) S-waves are completely reflected.

(b) P-waves are refracted away from the normal across the boundary.

(c) P-waves are refracted towards the normal across the boundary.

(d) S-waves stop at the boundary.

(e) P-waves are completely reflected.

(f) P-wave speed increases sharply.

TABLE 7   Properties of the Earth's interior

Layers and discontinuities	Depth to boundaries/km	Speed of P-waves/km s^{-1}	Percentage of total mass	Density/10^3 kg m^{-3}	Axial modulus/10^{11} N m^{-2}	Possible nature of layers	Possible nature of boundaries
CRUST	continental: 25–90 (average 35)	6.0	0.7	2.7	1.0	heterogeneous solids CONTINENTS: granitic OCEANS:	
	oceanic: 6–11	7.0		3.0	1.5	basaltic	CHEMICAL CHANGE from basalt or granite to peridotite
— Moho — UPPER		8.0		3.3	2.1	various types of peridotite	
low-speed layer	50–250	7.8				partly molten peridotite	PHASE CHANGE solid → solid and liquid → solid
MANTLE	400	8.2	68.0	3.4	2.3	solid peridotite	
transition zone	1 050	↓		↓	↓	↓	PHASE CHANGE to higher-density minerals
LOWER MANTLE		11.1		4.3	5.3	high-density minerals with overall peridotite	
	2 900	13.6		5.4	10.0	composition	CHEMICAL CHANGE from silicate mantle to iron-rich core
core–mantle OUTER CORE		8.1		9.9	6.5	probably iron + sulphur mixture (liquid)	
	5 155	10.1	31.3	12.3	12.5		CHEMICAL AND PHASE CHANGE
INNER CORE		11.2		13.5 (approx)	16.9	iron + nickel mixture (solid)	
	6 370	11.3					

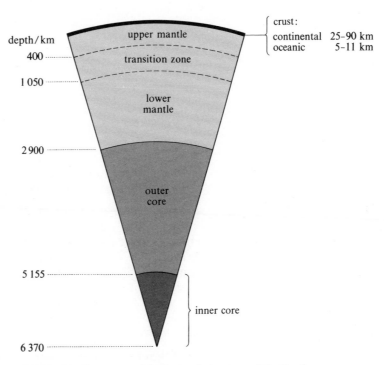

depth/km

crust: continental 25–90 km oceanic 5–11 km

upper mantle

400 — transition zone

1 050 — lower mantle

2 900 —

outer core

5 155 —

inner core

6 370 —

FIGURE 66   Summary of the layered structure of the Earth.

SAQ 24 Summarize in a few sentences the mechanism by which the Earth's magnetic field is thought to be generated.

SAQ 25 (a) What is the implication of the S-wave shadow zone for the nature of the material below the core–mantle boundary?

(b) List, and explain their relevance in one sentence each, four pieces of evidence that support the conclusion that the Earth's core is mostly iron, with sulphur in the outer core and nickel in the inner core.

SAQ 26 Using the information in your completed Table 6, the Colour Plates and the AV sequence 'Igneous rock formation', enter in the boxes in Figure 67 the rock sample numbers and names and Plate numbers corresponding to each of the seven locations shown.

FIGURE 67 Location of major igneous rock types (for use with SAQ 26).

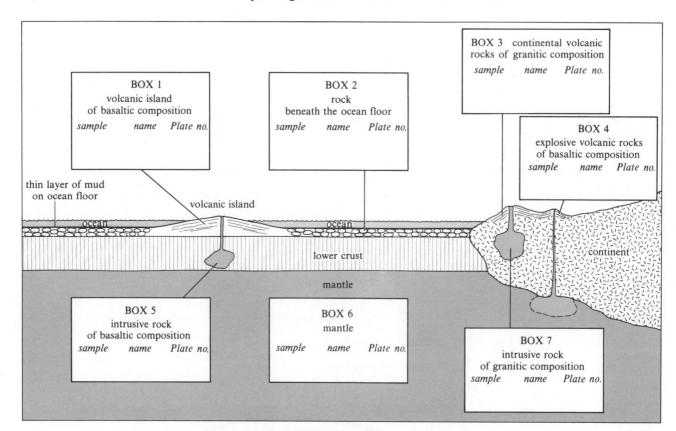

5 ROCK MAGNETISM (TV PROGRAMME)

The techniques described in this Section are illustrated further in the related TV programme 'Magnetic Earth' which also deals with many of the more important concepts arising from Sections 3 and 4.4.1.

The programme starts with an illustration of the inclination and declination of the Earth's magnetic field, first in the field in Iceland and then in the TV studio at Milton Keynes. The variation of magnetic inclination around the surface of the Earth is likened to that around a bar magnet with an axis inclined at 11° to the Earth's rotational axis (see Section 3, Figure 38). The programme illustrates the two-dimensional and then the three-dimensional alignment of iron filings around a bar magnet (which you should have seen in Experiment 2), leading to a description of what the Earth's magnetic field looks like today.

We then return to Iceland where some cores of old lava flows (Plates 22–23 at the back of this double Unit) are being studied by Leo Kristjansson of the University of Iceland. He uses a laboratory magnetometer to sense the direction of the magnetism recorded in the rocks, and this allows us to focus on the question: *Has the Earth's magnetic field always been as it is today?* As you will recall from Section 3.4 when we discussed secular variation, and dipole wobble in particular, we remarked that the strength and direction of the Earth's magnetic field at the time a rock formed can be determined from its palaeomagnetism. In the case of igneous rocks the magnetism is locked in as the rock solidifies and cools through its Curie temperature. However, in sedimentary rocks, any grains which are magnetic also become magnetized in the direction of the Earth's field as the rock is produced. To work out the direction of the Earth's magnetic field at the time a rock was formed, we need to know the orientation of the core sample in the ground when it was collected. Then, when the direction of magnetization in the sample has been measured, a simple calculation will give the magnetic direction (inclination) at the sampling site when the rock formed. The inclination is related to latitude in a simple way as we showed in Figure 38, and so the angular distance between the ancient or palaeomagnetic pole and the location in question can be derived as shown in Figure 68.

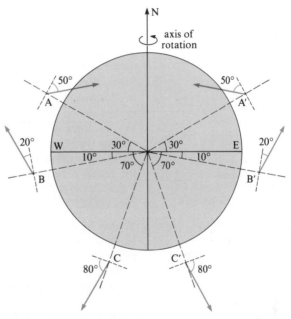

FIGURE 68 The relationship between angles of inclination, determined from oriented palaeomagnetic samples, and locations (A, B, C etc.) on the Earth's surface at the time each sample formed. The assumption is made that the Earth's magnetic field has, on average, always been that of an axially geocentric dipole. (Further details are given in the text.)

☐ The red arrows in Figure 68 (left-hand side) show examples of the angles of magnetic inclination at latitudes 30° N (A), 10° S (B) and 70° S (C). The inclination values are, respectively, $+50°$, $-20°$ and $-80°$. So there is a simple relationship whereby the latitude at which a rock formed (palaeolatitude) can be deduced from the inclination it preserves. But what about longitude? A′, B′ and C′ are also at 30° N, 10° S and 70° S respectively; what do you deduce about the relationship between magnetic inclination and longitude?

■ The inclination values are the same at A and A′, at B and B′, and at C and C′. So the longitude at which a rock formed (palaeolongitude) cannot be determined from magnetic inclination data; inclination is constant all around a line of latitude. Bear this in mind as you read on. (Remember also that palaeomagnetic studies have to assume that the magnetic field axis has been, on average, coincident with the Earth's axis of rotation.)

Palaeomagnetic investigations have revealed magnetism in rocks as old as 3 500 Ma (1 Ma = 10^6 years), showing that the Earth's magnetic field had developed by that time. This is not much less than the age of the oldest known crustal rocks and, as you will learn in Units 28–29, this compares with 4 600 Ma for the age of the Earth. Now we know that over the last few thousand years the magnetic field axis has on average coincided with the Earth's rotation axis, and that the field has been approximately dipolar. The magnetic inclinations from lavas formed over the last few million years in Iceland, some of which are analysed in the TV programme, also suggest

APPARENT POLAR WANDERING

that the distance between Iceland and the magnetic poles has been the same since they formed. Not surprisingly, however, those working with palaeomagnetic data wondered whether the coincidence between the magnetic and rotational axes has always been the case, and with the development during the decade after the Second World War of new techniques for investigating magnetization directions quickly and easily, they began to investigate older rocks from continental areas. This work also relied upon the development of more accurate methods of radioactive dating of rocks (about which you will learn more in Units 28–29), which began in 1911 with the pioneering work of, among others, the eminent geologist Arthur Holmes.

When the positions of palaeomagnetic poles for groups of rocks from particular continents older than a few million years are plotted, the poles appear *not* to have been close to the geographic poles.

ITQ 27 Can you think of *two* possible explanations for this?

The scientists who first discovered these deviations also noticed that the apparent positions of the poles for rocks of particular ages from one continent clustered together but that, sometimes (e.g. the data for Europe, Figure 69a), the positions of the clusters moved gradually away from the geographic poles the further back in time they were formed). This effect is called **apparent polar wandering**, and plots of the apparent positions of the poles, such as those in Figure 69, are called apparent polar wandering paths or 'curves'. What Figure 69a means (as suggested in the answer to ITQ 27) is that *either* Europe has been stationary and the magnetic north pole has moved from the Equator towards geographic north (from left to right) during the last 500 Ma, *or* that Europe has moved north (from right to left) during the same time. (Note that if the 500 Ma pole position was actually at the north geographic pole, Europe must have been at or to the south of the Equator on the right of the diagram. Europe must be moved right to bring the 500 Ma pole to the centre of Figure 69a.)

When the apparent wandering path of the pole for rocks from one continent was compared with the path for rocks from another, it became clear that the shapes of the two paths were radically different. This is illustrated in Figure 69b where the polar wandering curves for North America and for Europe are both shown.

□ What do you think could account for these differences? Does this exclude one of the possibilities deduced in ITQ 27?

FIGURE 69 Apparent polar wandering of the magnetic pole (a) for rocks from Europe formed within the last 500 Ma, and (b) for rocks from North America, compared with Europe, for the present positions of the continents. (In these projections you are looking down on the Northern Hemisphere of the Earth, as in Figure 50; the perimeter of each diagram represents the Equator.) Note that the polar wandering curves have been grossly simplified for use in this Course.

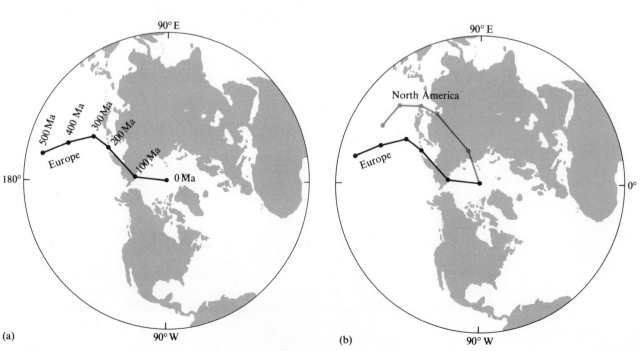

(a)   (b)

■ The only possible explanation is that the respective continents must have moved relative to the poles and to each other, since it is impossible that only the pole (i.e. with immobile continents) could move in such a way that the record of its positions on one continent could be different from the record of its positions on another.

For example, look at the apparent position of the pole at 500 Ma for Europe and for North America on Figure 69b. For Europe, the pole was apparently close to the Equator while, for North America, the apparent pole position is significantly further north. The use of the word 'significantly' is important here. Remember that a large number of observations have been summarized to produce each point plotted in Figure 69. The difference is only *significant* if the clusters of pole positions for each point in time do not overlap to any great extent, and if the average pole positions are different. Now if the two continents had not moved, the observations are paradoxical. The pole for Europe is in a different place from that for North America. The only possible explanation, as we have said, is that the continents must have moved *relative to each other*, and *relative to the pole*.

Note that if a continental area, such as North America in Figure 69b remains a unified whole, so that no part of the continent is moving relative to any other part, then the apparent position of the poles is the same for all parts of that continent. In other words, the position of the magnetic pole deduced from rock samples of a given age taken from New York is the same as it is for rocks of the same age from California. By an extension of this argument, if the whole continent is moving as one piece relative to the poles, the apparent polar wandering paths for every part of the continent will coincide.

ITQ 28 Bearing in mind the argument in the previous paragraph, what conclusion would you draw if the apparent polar wandering paths on two separate continents had the same *shape* from 400–100 Ma ago (as in Figure 69b), even though the paths were in different orientations?

What is the significance of the parts of the curves that do *not* have the same shapes? Well, if there had been palaeomagnetic experts on the Earth 100 Ma ago, and they were to have plotted the apparent polar wandering paths for two continents for the previous 300 Ma or so, then of course they would have had an identical path, because North America was rigidly joined to Europe over that period. This is illustrated in Figure 70, and you will note that we have had to bring Europe and North America closer together to make the two polar wandering paths for 400–100 Ma ago coincide.

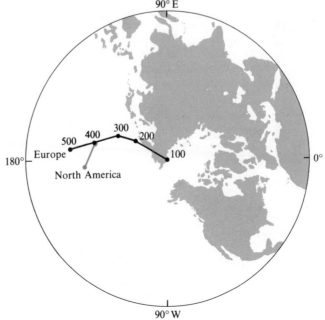

FIGURE 70 Apparent polar wandering paths for Europe and North America which would have been plotted 100 Ma ago for the preceding 400 Ma i.e. back to 500 Ma before today.

CONTINENTAL DRIFT

□ So what must have happened since 100 Ma ago for the paths to appear as in Figure 69b?

■ The only explanation possible is that Europe and North America have moved apart some time during the past 100 Ma.

To emphasize this point, if we took the maps and polar wandering paths plotted for the present positions of the continents (Figure 69b), and cut out with a pair of scissors the path for North America together with the outline of North America itself, we could then move the path and the bit of map so that the path for America coincided with that for Europe. Then the outline of the east coast of North America would fit snugly with the western seaboard of Europe, which is where North America must have been from 400–100 Ma ago before it drifted away to open up the north Atlantic. Now you will remember that we referred earlier to the problem of deducing palaeolongitude from inclination data. You might, therefore, wonder how we fix pole positions in the way shown in Figures 69 and 70. This is done using the present positions of the continents in Figure 69 and their best-fit positions in Figure 70. Once the position of a continent is fixed in space, the horizontal direction and inclination of palaeomagnetic samples define a *unique* pole position in plots such as those in Figures 69 and 70. So you can see that our ignorance of palaeolongitudes is not quite such a limitation as it might seem at first sight. Notice one other feature of Figure 70: the two polar wandering curves are separate during the period from 400–500 Ma ago.

□ What might this imply?

■ That Europe and North America were *not* joined prior to 400 Ma ago. (In fact they came together and moved in unison for 300 Ma before separating again to form the modern Atlantic).

As Earth scientists were obliged, in some cases reluctantly, to come to the same kind of conclusions as you have just reached, so the theory of **continental drift**, which had waxed and waned in popularity since it was first proposed as long ago as 1858, finally became generally accepted during the 1960s. (You will learn more about this in Units 7–8.) The theory implies, as its name suggests, that continents move apparently independently over the surface of the Earth.

One more piece of palaeomagnetic evidence is needed in developing the theory and that concerns the *reversals* of magnetic polarity which we first mentioned in Section 3.4. But why should the magnetic field totally reverse its polarity? That's the fundamental point we shall now consider. Although there are a few materials which show the property of alternating magnetism as their physical characteristics change, these materials are not common as rock-forming minerals, and this phenomenon of 'self-reversal', as it is called, cannot account for the extent and variety of rocks with reversed palaeomagnetism. Furthermore, whether or not a particular rock shows reversed magnetism depends not upon the type of rock, but upon its *age*, confirming the idea that the Earth's magnetic field has been reversed for certain periods of the Earth's history.

The fact that all rocks of a known age have the same polarity was first conclusively established by Allan Cox and Richard Doell of the US Geological Survey in the 1960s. They collected a large variety of 'young' rocks, measured their polarities, and dated them accurately. This work enabled them to build up a polarity time-scale, which is shown in Figure 71. This shows *epochs* which are periods of predominantly one polarity, and *events* which are shorter periods within epochs when the field was briefly of the opposite polarity.

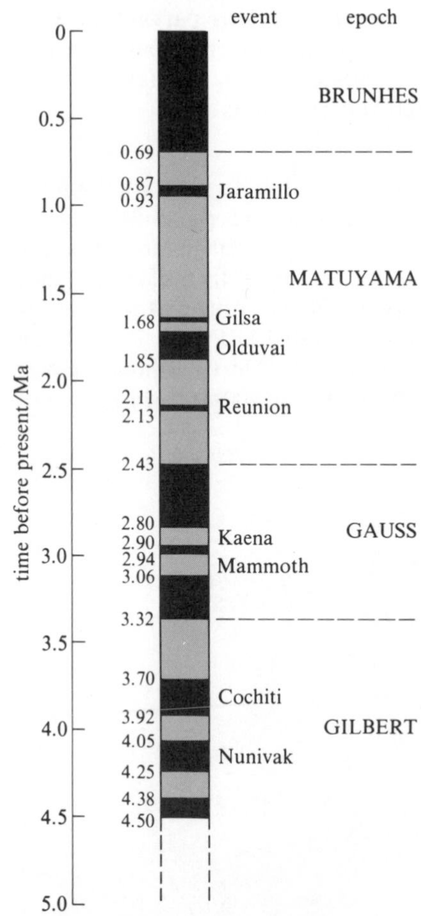

As more and more rocks were dated and the directions of magnetization established, a picture was built up of repeated periods of reversed field, alternating with periods during which the field was normal, that is to say, the same as it is today. The results of some of these investigations are shown in Figure 72. There is now evidence that *field reversals have occurred throughout as much of geological time as has been investigated* (i.e. way back even beyond the period shown in Figure 72).

FIGURE 71   The polarity time-scale for the last 4.5 Ma. This scale may not be complete since there are probably short events still to be discovered. Normal magnetic periods are shown in black, and reversed periods in grey.

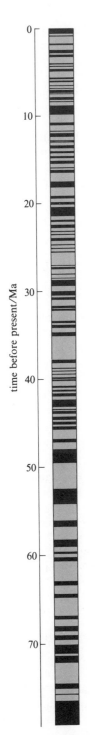

FIGURE 72   Polarity time-scale for the last 80 Ma of the Earth's history. Normal periods are shown in black, and reversed periods in grey.

Note that there may well be some short periods of reversal that have not yet been detected and are therefore not shown on Figure 72. Detection depends upon availability of suitable rocks of the right age, and also upon the precision with which the age of rocks can be established. If we can only work out the age of a rock which is about 50 Ma old to within 3 Ma, then clearly we are not going to be able to distinguish a reversed period at 52–51 Ma from one which occurred at 50–49 Ma ago.

The discovery of these reversals of the Earth's magnetic field is consistent with the self-exciting dynamo model for the origin of the field. Such rapid changes can only occur if the field is produced by some dynamic process such as we discussed in Section 4.4.1. If the electric currents reverse their direction, then the magnetic field direction will also be reversed. Various models for producing field reversals are illustrated in the TV programme; they all relate in some way to the self-exciting dynamo (Figure 61). Remember that models for the origin of the Earth's magnetic field must account for the rapid westward drift of the non-dipole field component as well as for the phenomenon of field reversals.

Close investigation of how the field reversals actually take place has now been carried out using palaeomagnetism. The positions of the magnetic poles appear to wander aimlessly about over a period of about 10 000 years before settling down to their new direction and the strength of the field reduces to about 10% of its average value. The actual mechanism by which reversals take place and the cause of reversals are not known. Presumably a reversed field results when the helical electrical currents, which are thought to be the source of the field, reverse their direction. The reversal episode must begin by a break-down in the helical shapes of the currents, and the currents must become more or less random before their helical shape is re-established. There is inconclusive evidence of episodes in which the currents cease to be regular for a time before the pattern is resumed without a reversal having taken place.

Although these reversal episodes appear to take around 10 000 years to complete, this is a relatively short time, and you should remember that, *on average*, the Earth's magnetic field has been approximately that of an axially-centred dipole. The discovery of field reversals was a great surprise and this, together with the implications of apparent polar wandering curves, led to a major conceptual revolution in Earth sciences. In the TV programme we start to illustrate the implications of field reversals for the palaeomagnetism locked in rocks of the ocean floor around Iceland. The ideas derived from studies of anomalous magnetism in these rocks was largely instrumental in generating the theory of *sea-floor spreading*. According to this theory, molten material welling-up at ocean ridges crystallizes and spreads away to either side as new material is continuously injected into the ridge system. We defer the details of this process and the role of magnetic reversals in the understanding of sea-floor spreading until Units 7–8.

SUMMARY OF SECTION 5

1   The Earth has had a magnetic field for at least 3 500 Ma, and it is thought that the field has, on average, been that of a dipole.

2   The Earth's magnetic field has undergone many reversals of polarity.

3   Studies of palaeomagnetic pole positions for rocks of particular ages from different continents show apparent wandering of the magnetic poles, which implies that the continents themselves have been in motion.

4   The restoration of continents back to their original positions by aligning parts of their respective apparent polar wandering paths shows the relative positions of the continents at past moments in time.

5   The occurrence of field reversals is consistent with the self-exciting dynamo model for the origin of the Earth's magnetic field.

SAQ 27   How can we be sure that magnetic field reversals have really taken place, and that the reversed magnetization found in some rocks is not just a result of a particular property of the rock?

SAQ 28   What are apparent polar wandering paths, and what is their significance?

SAQ 29   What do we learn from fitting together the similarly shaped parts of apparent polar wandering paths for two different continents?

6 SOME USES OF MAGNETIC AND SEISMIC TECHNIQUES

Now that you have seen how Earth scientists study the interior of the Earth you may be thinking: Yes, but what use is it all? This Section explains some uses of the seismic and magnetic studies which have been the focus of this double Unit. It will, necessarily, present a picture which is briefer and simpler than reality but should give you some idea of the scope of these techniques for practising scientists and, indirectly, for the general public.

6.1 MAGNETIC SURVEYING

What do you think might happen to the needle of a compass suspended from an aircraft, as it is flown over rocks rich in iron, and why? The compass needle would be deflected from pointing north and would be drawn towards the iron-rich rocks, because their magnetic field strength will locally distort the Earth's magnetic field. This is nothing to do with the non-dipole field component but is due to the intense permanent magnetism of the rocks. For example, there are mountains in Sweden consisting almost entirely of pure iron ore and there are similar deposits in the Lake Superior area of North America.

ITQ 29   Can you now briefly suggest a way of prospecting for deposits of iron in a remote and inhospitable region?

The compass-like instrument mentioned in the answer to ITQ 29 is a called a **magnetometer** and aerial surveying in this way, or **magnetic prospecting**, is a common preliminary technique when large areas are to be covered and expeditions in the field would be difficult because of a hostile climate or poor communications. Magnetic surveys are also useful to show the gross distribution of rocks of different magnetic character. Aerial magnetic surveying on a global scale also enables a check to be kept on changes to both the overall magnetic field and to the positions of the poles.

6.2 SEISMIC TECHNIQUES IN THE OIL INDUSTRY

In recent decades, geologists have discovered that they can learn a lot about the detailed structure of rock formations using small, artificial earthquakes. These are caused by setting off a series of small explosive charges in defined places and recording the results with seismometers. These techniques are particularly useful for offshore oil prospecting: a ship tows a sound source, the sound waves are reflected at the junctions of rock layers and these reflected waves return to the surface where they are recorded by the seis-

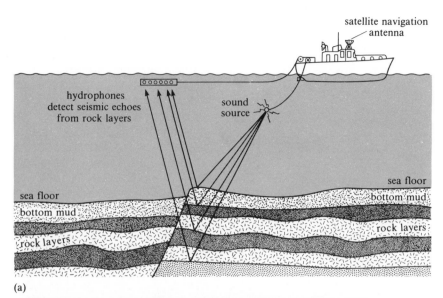

FIGURE 73 (a) Seismic method of prospecting for oil and gas offshore—general principle.

(a)

FIGURE 73 (b) Example of a seismic reflection profile (seismic section) from the Gulf of Mexico, 30 km long and 10 km deep, in which folded sedimentary layers are revealed by reflected seismic waves. The light and dark bands are produced where there are strong contrasts in the reflective properties of the rocks.

(b)

mometers, in this context called *hydrophones*. The procedure is shown in Figure 73a and an example of a **reflection profile** in 73b. The interpretation of the profile is that the rocks are arched into a dome in the centre. Petroleum geologists spend much of their time searching for structures like the one shown in Figure 73b.

ITQ 30 Can you think of a reason why domes such as that shown in Figure 73b are of interest to petroleum geologists? (Hint: The sediments contain water in their pore spaces and oil has a lower density than water.)

6.3 DETECTING AND MONITORING NUCLEAR EXPLOSIONS

You saw in Table 2 (Section 1) approximate values for the energy released through earthquakes and explosions of various magnitudes and you may have realized (from the TV programme 'Earthquakes—seismology at work') that seismometers around the world will record similar traces for these events. However, there are crucial differences between earthquakes and explosions which might form the basis of a detection and monitoring system.

☐ How do explosions differ from earthquakes with respect to depth, magnitude and location?

■ Explosions take place high up in the crust whereas earthquake foci tend to be deeper. Earthquakes generally have a greater magnitude than explosions and occur in seismic zones (see Figure 13) whereas explosions can be arranged practically anywhere.

The relative sizes of the events and their locations are not particularly reliable arguments for distinguishing an explosion from an earthquake, so we need a clearer method of recognizing explosions if we are to monitor international agreements on reducing underground nuclear testing. Such arguments concern the nature of the seismic traces obtained from an explosion and an earthquake. The shock wave generated by an explosion will have the characteristics of a large energy release from a point source; that is, the first component will be compressional in all directions. *All* receiving seismometers will therefore receive a first P-wave that is a compressional wave. Also, the radial release of energy from an explosion does not initially generate any shear waves like those associated with movement of a fault. Earthquakes, on the other hand, result from ruptures associated with fault planes (see Figures 10 and 11) and although there are first shocks that are compressional in some directions, there are also *dilatations* (first movements of the ground *towards* the epicentre) in others; these differences are shown schematically in Figure 74.

FIGURE 74 (a) Explosion: all first motions away from source; (b) earthquake: showing varied compressional and dilatational first motions.

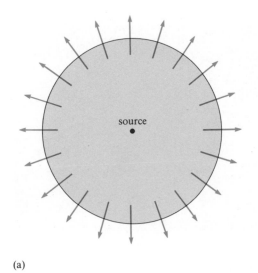

(a)

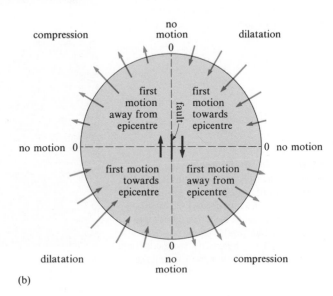

(b)

Compressions are recorded as first movements *upwards* on a seismic trace of a vertical seismogram, whereas dilatations are recorded as first movements *downwards*. Thus earthquakes and explosions can be distinguished according to the seismic traces they produce.

ITQ 31 With reference to Figure 74, briefly describe the differences between the first arrivals of P-waves from earthquakes and explosions as recorded by a network of seismometers.

A relationship has also been established between the *body* waves (the P- and S-waves you have been learning about) and the *surface* waves (the L-waves of Figure 25, which we have not discussed in detail). This relationship is shown in Figure 75.

☐ Using Figure 75, briefly explain the difference between the waves produced by explosions and those produced by earthquakes.

■ Explosions produce higher magnitude body waves (those that pass through the Earth) whereas earthquakes produce higher magnitude surface waves.

At the time of writing, scientists in the USA, Europe and the USSR were agreed that seismology can detect and distinguish underground nuclear explosions down to a level of about one kilotonne (equivalent to a magnitude 4 earthquake). Together with remote sensing, this could provide the scientific basis of a monitoring system for the detection of underground nuclear tests.

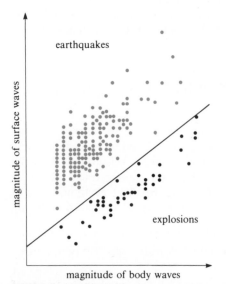

FIGURE 75 Relationship between the body wave and surface wave magnitudes of explosions and earthquakes.

6.4 EARTHQUAKE PREDICTION

The ultimate test of our understanding of earthquakes and their mechanisms is to predict successfully where and when large earthquakes will happen.

ITQ 32 (a) What do you think are the chances that a 'great' earthquake (magnitude more than 8 on the Richter scale) will occur in Britain this century?

(b) What are the chances that a 'great' earthquake will occur in China before the end of this century?

At one level, therefore, we have made advances in earthquake prediction at a gross scale. However, for people at risk, prediction has to be accurate to two or three days, not a high-risk possibility in the next 20–30 years. One notable success at this scale was the prediction of a major event at Haicheng in China in 1975 (Figure 76). How was this done?

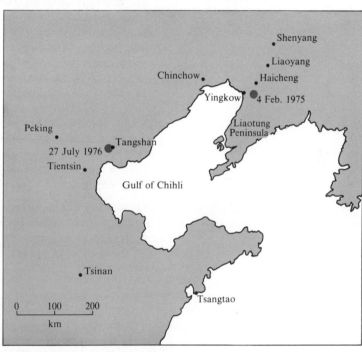

FIGURE 76 Location map for the large Chinese earthquakes of 1975 and 1976.

By involving both experts, amateurs and local workers, the Chinese collected data on a number of factors that they felt might help pinpoint an earthquake's location and time. These included surface deformation (for example bulging) and strain in the Earth, seismic wave patterns and speeds, magnetic patterns, the water level in wells, the concentration of radon (a radioactive gas) in groundwater and even the behaviour of animals! They found that vertical deformation north of the Liaotung Peninsula had increased by a factor of 20 since the 1960s and had doubled in 1973 and 1974.

Three particular areas were identified as being at greatest risk and these were examined closely. During late 1974, observers reported water spouting from the ground, large numbers of small earthquakes and an increase in restlessness amongst the animals. At 10.00 a.m. on 4 February 1975 the warning was given to expect an earthquake within two days between Haicheng and Yingkow, 50 km to the south-west. The earthquake struck 9 hours and 36 minutes later, and was larger than the Richter magnitude 6 that was anticipated. Yet because of the warning, people were not inside buildings when the earthquake happened and so there were few fatalities.

However, the Chinese are not always successful. For example they did not predict the 1976 Tangshan event (Figure 76) which killed a large number of people (estimates vary between a quarter and three-quarters of a million). It has been reported that this earthquake was not heralded by small earthquake foreshocks, increasing in frequency, which were the precursors of the Haicheng event.

In the USA, efforts at prediction have been concentrated on the San Andreas Fault System (SAFS).

☐ Why do you think most interest has focused here?

■ Because this is a seismic zone (Figure 13) where earthquakes have happened regularly, and because of the large population and high level of industrialization, there is a considerable potential for extremely costly damage in human and material terms.

It has been estimated that a severe earthquake on the San Andreas Fault at 2.30 in the morning might kill about 3 000 people, whereas at 4.30 in the afternoon 13 000 deaths might be caused.

☐ Suggest a few factors and reasons that might account for the difference between these estimates.

■ At 2.30 a.m. most people are at home in bed; and their houses, which are generally of wood-framed construction, are designed to resist structural damage. At 4.30 p.m., many people are on the freeways and in high-rise downtown areas; an earthquake would cause traffic accidents, and people would be at risk from falling glass and masonry. Also, many of the older municipal buildings in the centre of most towns and cities are not reinforced and would be likely to collapse in an earthquake of moderate strength, resulting in many fatalities.

Although the loss of life is the main consideration, the disruption of the road system, power, gas and telephone lines, and damage to dams and culverts taking water to the cities from reservoirs, would all lead to serious difficulties after an earthquake, so for the authorities and utility companies, earthquake prediction is also important.

The epicentres of Californian earthquakes have been plotted on maps and from this pattern it has been deduced that the SAFS behaves differently along its length (Figure 77). In the northern section (Section I) the last major movement, of up to 6 m, was during the 1906 San Francisco earthquake; similarly, there was a major movement and earthquake on Section

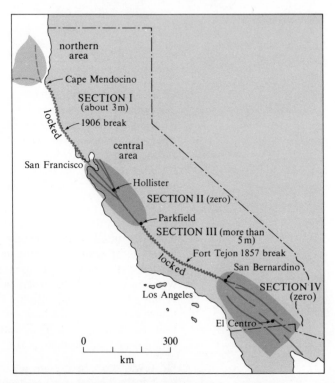

FIGURE 77 Potential 'slippage' accumulated in the rocks of the San Andreas Fault System (SAFS). The fault is divided here into four sections and the potential slippage (in metres) due to the accumulated strain is indicated where known. Active sections of the fault are shaded; 'locked' sections are indicated by a zig-zag line.

III in 1857 at Fort Tejon. Since those times, strain has been accumulating along the fault and the amount of stored 'potential slippage' for each section is indicated on Figure 77.

ITQ 33   In Section II of the San Andreas Fault System, shown in Figure 77, there have been no major earthquakes and no potential slippage is accumulating; can you suggest why this is so?

The south-east part of Section III of the SAFS has not produced a major earthquake during the past 200 years and the study of layered deposits in stream valleys indicates that this probably extends to about 550 years, yet creep is not occurring here. It has been estimated that at least 11 m of potential slippage is already stored in this part of the fault. Similar studies indicate that in Sections I and III major earthquakes with several metres slippage are likely once every 150 years on average. The 1857 Fort Tejon and the 1906 San Francisco events were the last major earthquakes in these sections of the SAFS, so the chances of a major earthquake happening in the next 30 years or so are very high for the region to the East of Los Angeles and only a little less for the San Francisco area.

It would appear, therefore, that there has been little real progress in the science of earthquake prediction at the local scale. However, in California, networks of seismometers have been installed to measure the small earthquakes that might precede 'the big one' that most Californians expect. There are also instruments measuring the tilting of the ground and the strain in the rocks, together with other indicators, such as the electrical resistance of rocks and the pressure of water in rock pore spaces. It appears that the people of California have not been instructed to observe and report any abnormal behaviour in their animals as the Chinese were, but what might be considered abnormal behaviour in rural China might pass totally unnoticed in California!

SUMMARY OF SECTION 6

1   Magnetic techniques can be used for mapping the gross magnetic features of an area, and are therefore useful in ore prospecting, particularly where the associated rocks are magnetic.

2   Seismic reflection techniques can be used to determine the structure of rock formations. This is particularly useful for offshore prospecting in the oil industry.

3   Seismic techniques and the examination of seismic traces can be used to distinguish between earthquakes and underground nuclear explosions.

4   There has been some progress in the prediction of earthquakes but much remains to be investigated at the detailed level. Efforts are concentrated on understanding the physical changes taking place in the rock strata of earthquake-prone areas prior to major shocks.

SAQ 30   The best estimate of average rate of movement of the San Andreas Fault is 2 cm per year (see Figure 12) and the distance from Los Angeles to San Francisco is about 800 km. At this rate of movement, when is Los Angeles due to become a suburb of San Francisco?

OBJECTIVES FOR UNITS 5–6

After you have worked through this double Unit, you should be able to:

1 Explain the meaning of, and use correctly, all the terms flagged in the text.

2 Explain the characteristics of and differences between the two scales used to measure earthquakes: the Richter magnitude scale and the Mercalli intensity scale. (*SAQ 1*)

3 Describe briefly, and in qualitative terms, the mechanisms involved in three types of faulting. (*ITQ 4, SAQ 2*)

4 Describe, in qualitative terms, how seismometers work. (*1st TV*)

5 Explain the different characteristics of igneous and sedimentary rocks, and correctly identify igneous and sedimentary textures in hand specimens. (*SAQ 3, 1st AV*)

6 Explain the differences between intrusive and extrusive igneous rocks. (*2nd AV, SAQ 26*)

7 Explain how texture and the kinds of mineral grains present can be used to classify rocks. (*1st AV, 2nd AV*)

8 Explain how the cooling rate of a magma determines crystal size in the resulting rock. (*2nd AV*)

9 Match igneous rock types to their place of formation in the crust or mantle. (*SAQ 26*)

10 Explain by giving an example, that what is propagated by a pressure wave down a row of balls and springs, or by a seismic wave, is not the medium but a disturbance. (*ITQs 8 and 9*)

11 Explain how the speed of a wave varies when the stiffness (i.e. the elastic moduli) or the density of the propagating medium is changed. (*ITQ 12, SAQ 8*)

12 Explain in simple terms why an S-wave cannot pass through a liquid. (*SAQ 6*)

13 Recall the equations enabling you to calculate the speeds of P- and S-waves through a medium given the values of the elastic moduli and the density. (*ITQ 13, SAQ 7*)

14 State Snell's law of refraction and apply it to calculate the angle of refraction for any given angle of incidence for a wave crossing a seismic boundary. (*ITQ 14, SAQ 9*)

15 State the relationship between the angle of incidence and the angle of reflection of a wave reflected at a boundary. (*ITQ 15*)

16 Predict whether total internal reflection of a wave will occur at a boundary, given the wave speeds on either side of the boundary. (*SAQ 11*)

17 Explain qualitatively the phenomenon of continuous refraction. (*SAQ 12*)

18 Explain qualitatively the ways in which bar magnets interact. (*SAQ 13*)

19 Explain in simple terms the concept of a magnetic field. (*Experiment 1, ITQs 16 and 18*)

20 Describe the shape and properties of a dipolar magnetic field. (*Experiment 2, ITQ 17, SAQ 14*)

21 Describe the overall shape and orientation of the Earth's dipolar magnetic field. (*ITQ 19, SAQ 17*)

22 Describe how the Earth's magnetic field varies in both strength and direction. (*ITQ 19*)

23 Describe the nature of the difference between the actual magnetic field and the theoretical dipole field of the Earth, and how these differences vary with time. (*SAQ 15*)

24 Explain the significance of the non-dipole field variations to theories of the origin of the Earth's magnetic field. (*SAQ 16*)

25 Explain the meaning of the Curie temperature, and its relevance to theories of the origin of the Earth's magnetic field. (*Experiment 3, ITQ 20*)

26   Understand the mechanism of rock magnetization and the concepts of normal and reversed polarity in rocks. (*SAQ 27*)

27   Draw correct conclusions about the variation of elastic moduli and density with depth within the Earth, given seismic wave travel times and relevant data on surface rocks. (*ITQs 12 and 13, SAQ 8*)

28   Describe a plausible model for the internal structure of the Earth, given data on P- and S-wave shadow zones and on seismic travel times. (*SAQ 20*)

29   Summarize the seismic evidence for the liquid nature of the outer core, and the nature of the changes across the core–mantle boundary. (*ITQs 24–26, SAQ 23*)

30   Briefly state the seismic evidence for the existence of the solid inner core. (*ITQ 24, SAQ 25*)

31   Describe a plausible model for the origin of the Earth's magnetic field, and summarize those features of the field that the model explains. (*SAQ 24*)

32   Summarize the theoretical, observational and experimental evidence for the composition of the inner and outer core. (*ITQ 24*)

33   Describe the broad features of the internal structure of the mantle, with particular reference to the importance of phase changes of the mantle materials. (*SAQ 21*)

34   Describe briefly the nature of the crust, and the variation in depth of its lower boundary (the Mohorovičić discontinuity). (*2nd AV*)

35   Draw a sketch cross-section of the Earth's interior, showing the principal layers, their boundaries and their probable compositions. (*SAQ 19*)

36   Explain how magnetic inclination data for ancient rocks can be used to determine palaeolatitudes. (*SAQ 27*)

37   Describe how palaeomagnetic data, in the form of apparent polar wandering paths, can be used to deduce the previous positions of continents. (*ITQ 28, SAQ 29*)

38   Describe, in simple terms, how magnetic prospecting and seismic reflection profiles can be used to interpret subsurface geological structures. (*ITQs 29 and 30*)

39   Describe, in simple terms, the ways in which seismic data can be used to distinguish between earthquakes and underground nuclear explosions. (*ITQ 31*)

40   Give a brief summary of progress in the prediction of earthquakes. (*ITQ 32*)

ITQ ANSWERS AND COMMENTS

ITQ 1 (a) 1:320; 0.31%.

Total relief = $8\,850\,\text{m} + 11\,000\,\text{m} = 19\,850\,\text{m}$, or approximately 19.9 km. Because the radius of Earth is 6 370 km, the ratio of relief to the Earth's radius is 19.9:6 370, or about 1:320.

As a percentage this is $(1/320) \times 100\% \approx 0.31\%$, or about one-third of one per cent! So the total relief of the Earth's surface is only a tiny fraction of the Earth's radius.

(b) If the radius of the circle drawn for the Earth is 5 cm, the total relief should be

$$(5\,\text{cm} \times 0.31)/100 = (5 \times 0.31\,\text{mm})/10$$

$$= 0.16\,\text{mm (to 2 significant figures).}$$

In other words, the drawn line (of width 0.2 mm) would be *thicker* than the line (of width 0.16 mm) that correctly represents the total relief of the Earth, if this were drawn to scale.

ITQ 2 50 km.

An average rise of 2 °C per 100 m implies that a rise of 1 000 °C corresponds to a depth of

$$\frac{1\,000\,°\text{C}}{2\,°\text{C}} \times 100\,\text{m} = 5 \times 10^4\,\text{m}$$

$$= 50\,\text{km}$$

ITQ 3 $5.5 \times 10^9\,\text{N}\,\text{m}^{-2}$.

Pressure = $h\rho g$ (2)*

$$= 10^5\,\text{m} \times (5.5 \times 10^3\,\text{kg}\,\text{m}^{-3}) \times 10\,\text{m}\,\text{s}^{-2}$$

$$= 5.5 \times 10^9\,\text{N}\,\text{m}^{-2}$$

This is much greater than the pressure due to the atmosphere at the Earth's surface, $10^5\,\text{N}\,\text{m}^{-2}$ (approx.).

ITQ 4 The linear feature from the top to the bottom of Plate 2a is the fault. This is also shown running across Plate 2b, as illustrated in Figure 78. The evidence for faulting is that the rivers have been displaced; A_1

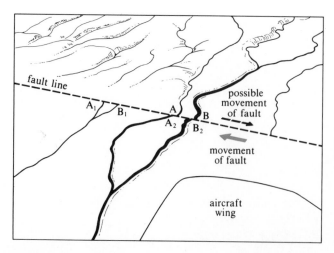

FIGURE 78 Fault motions deduced from off-set stream channels (for ITQ 4).

and B_1 were, at some time in the past, aligned with A and B. More recently, A_2 and B_2 have been displaced from A and B. The *relative* movement is indicated by the fact that the area at the bottom of the photograph has moved to the left (and slightly towards the top of the page), and/or that the top right of the photograph has moved to the right. This relative movement is shown in the Figure. Because of other evidence, we know that the *actual* movement is that the area on the bottom part of the photograph moved to the left, but this cannot be decided from this photograph alone.

ITQ 5 (a) Earthquakes are found to occur in several distinct regions. One region surrounds the Pacific Ocean—the Circum-Pacific Belt; this is often referred to as the 'ring of fire' because of its active volcanism, and it accounts for the fact that Japan, Alaska and the whole of the western coast of North and South America are frequently in the news as sites of earthquakes. There is another zone of earthquakes, from south-eastern Europe through the Middle East and the Himalayan Mountains: the Alpine–Himalayan Belt. There are also earthquakes down the middle of the Atlantic Ocean and in linear zones in other oceans.

(b) The earthquakes around the Pacific are located under the mountains and trenches that surround that ocean (for example, near the coast of South America, or off the coast of Japan). The earthquakes through Europe and the Himalayas also appear to be associated with mountain ranges. Even the earthquakes in the oceans appear to be associated with the relief depicted there. The feature shown down the Atlantic is called, predictably, the Mid-Atlantic Ridge and there are other ridges which have associated earthquakes. (The story of how and why this is so is the subject of Units 7–8.)

ITQ 6 At a depth of 700 km, the rocks will be very hot and under great pressure and they will *flow* rather than fracture, or fault (think of the answer to ITQ 2 and of the snow and ice analogy). If there is no sudden energy release due to faulting, there will be no earthquake.

ITQ 7 Three units on the Richter scale represent a factor of 10^3 (i.e. 1 000) increase in the maximum amount of ground motion caused by the earthquake. Remember, the scale is logarithmic.

ITQ 8 The completed graph is shown in Figure 79.

(a) Yes, it is a smooth curve.

(b) Yes, the displacement rises and falls to the same maxima (and the same minima) in a regular way.

(c) This regular wave-like disturbance repeats itself after 180 ms.

ITQ 9 (a) The block shaded in black in Figure 24 is squashed, or sheared out of shape first in one direction, then in the other at right angles to the (left–right) direction of wave propagation. Clearly, its shape is changing, but its total area and, therefore, the volume of material behind this front face in the diagram appears to remain unchanged.

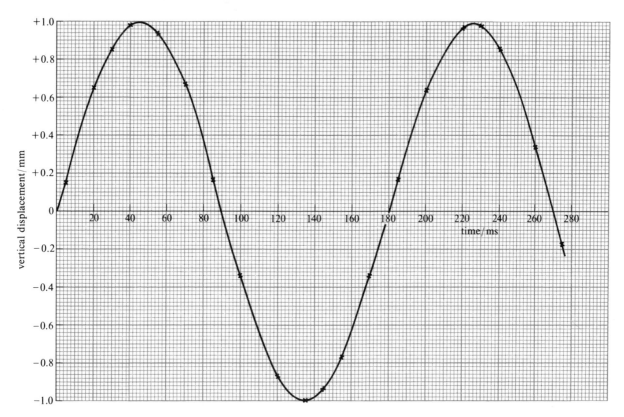

FIGURE 79 Completed graph of vertical displacement against time (for ITQ 8).

(b) The lack of volume change during the propagation of transverse waves is different to that occurring for P-waves, where there is a change in volume but no change in the basic rectangular shape (the block is squashed and stretched but remains rectangular with 90° angles between the faces: Figure 22).

ITQ 10 (a) You may have found it intuitively obvious that propagation will be slower in a denser medium, but if not try the following reasoning. From Newton's second law of motion, if we increase m, a given force will produce a smaller acceleration and hence a smaller initial speed. So, in Figure 21, if the balls had *greater mass*, a given force would cause the compression pulse to travel *more slowly*. If we consider what happens within a rock we can think of a small fixed volume of the rock that is being vibrated (see Figure 22). Increasing the mass of this small fixed volume would therefore result in the P-wave motion being transmitted more slowly.

(b) Stiffer springs will lead to faster P-wave propagation if the mass of the balls remains unchanged. For example, consider the following: a strong (i.e. stiff) spring will return more quickly to its original length than a weak spring for a particular amount of extension. Of course, it will also require a larger force to extend a stiff spring by the same amount. Since a stronger spring will contract back more quickly, it follows that it will vibrate more quickly than a weaker spring. Consequently, in our ball and spring model, a ball will set the next ball in the line vibrating more quickly with stronger springs than with weaker springs. Since we are talking about compression in rocks, it follows that rocks which are less easily compressed will transmit seismic P-waves *more rapidly* than those which

are more easily compressed, all other things being equal. (Alternatively, since with strong springs we require a larger initial force to produce the same amplitude of disturbance at the other end of the line, from Newton's second law, the greater will be the acceleration and hence the greater the resulting speed.)

ITQ 11 (a) $(length)^2 \times (time)^{-2}$.

In SI units axial modulus (ψ) is measured in $N\,m^{-2}$.

We know (from Unit 3) that $1\,N = 1\,kg\,m\,s^{-2}$

Therefore the units of ψ are

$$(kg\,m\,s^{-2}) \times m^{-2} = kg\,m^{-1}\,s^{-2}$$

So the dimensions of ψ are

$$(mass) \times (length)^{-1} \times (time)^{-2}$$

Density (ρ) is measured in $kg\,m^{-3}$, which has the dimensions: $(mass) \times (length)^{-3}$.

The dimensions of the ratio ψ/ρ are therefore:

$$\frac{(mass) \times (length)^{-1} \times (time)^{-2}}{(mass) \times (length)^{-3}}$$

$$= (length)^2 \times (time)^{-2}$$

cf. dimensions of speed: $(length) \times (time)^{-1}$.

(b) $v_P \propto \sqrt{\psi/\rho}$.

A dimensionally correct relationship must have the same dimensions on both sides. This can be achieved by taking the square root of ψ/ρ, thus converting its dimensions from $(length)^2 \times (time)^{-2}$ into $(length) \times (time)^{-1}$. We can then write:

$$v_P \propto \sqrt{\psi/\rho}$$

This is the correct relationship between v_P, ψ and ρ. Please do not worry if you were unable to deduce this relationship so long as you have followed our reasoning.

ITQ 12 (a) v_P increases by factors of 1.41, 1.73 and 2.00, respectively.

We know that $v_P = \sqrt{\dfrac{\psi}{\rho}}$ (9)*

So if density does not change, but axial modulus increases by a factor of 2, we can express the change as follows:

If the original $v_P = \sqrt{\dfrac{\psi}{\rho}}$, the new $v_P = \sqrt{\dfrac{2\psi}{\rho}}$,

so the new v_P is $\sqrt{2}$ times the previous v_P.

In other words, when ψ increases by a factor of 2, v_P increases by a factor of $\sqrt{2} = 1.41$.

Similarly, if ψ increases by factors of 3 and 4, v_P increases by: $\sqrt{3} = 1.73$, and $\sqrt{4} = 2.00$, respectively.

(b) Conversely, if axial modulus does not change, v_P will *decrease* with increasing density by the same factors, i.e. by $\sqrt{2}$, $\sqrt{3}$ and $\sqrt{4}$.

ITQ 13 $v_P = 7.4 \, \text{km s}^{-1}$; $v_S = 3.8 \, \text{km s}^{-1}$.

For P-waves,

$$v_P = \sqrt{\dfrac{\psi}{\rho}} \qquad (9)*$$

Substituting the values of ψ and ρ given, we have:

$$v_P = \sqrt{\dfrac{3 \times 10^{11}}{5.5 \times 10^3}} \, \text{m s}^{-1}$$

$$= \sqrt{5.45 \times 10^7} \, \text{m s}^{-1}$$

$$= 7.38 \times 10^3 \, \text{m s}^{-1}$$

$$= 7.4 \, \text{km s}^{-1} \text{ (to 2 significant figures)}$$

Similarly, for S-waves,

$$v_S = \sqrt{\dfrac{\mu}{\rho}} \qquad (11)*$$

Hence:

$$v_S = \sqrt{\dfrac{8 \times 10^{10}}{5.5 \times 10^3}} \, \text{m s}^{-1}$$

$$= \sqrt{14.5 \times 10^6} \, \text{m s}^{-1}$$

$$= 3.81 \times 10^3 \, \text{m s}^{-1}$$

$$= 3.8 \, \text{km s}^{-1} \text{ (to 2 significant figures)}$$

It is interesting to note that both P- and S-waves travel much faster than Concorde, which has a cruising speed of about $0.66 \, \text{km s}^{-1}$.

ITQ 14 (a) 74.6°.

Using Snell's law:

$$\dfrac{\sin i}{\sin r} = \dfrac{v_1}{v_2} \qquad (12)*$$

When $v_2 = 1.5 v_1$

$$\dfrac{\sin i}{\sin r} = \dfrac{1}{1.5}$$

Hence $\sin r = 1.5 \sin i$

$$= 1.5 \sin 40°$$

$$= 1.5 \times 0.6428$$

$$= 0.9642$$

whence the angle of refraction $r = 74.6°$.

(b) 25.4°.

Similarly, when $v_1 = 1.5 v_2$

$$\dfrac{\sin i}{\sin r} = 1.5$$

Hence $\sin r = \dfrac{\sin i}{1.5}$

$$= \dfrac{0.6428}{1.5}$$

$$= 0.4285$$

whence the angle of refraction $r = 25.4°$.

(c) When a wave travels into a medium where the propagation speed is *higher*, it is bent *away* from the normal (as in part a) and when it passes into a medium where the speed is *lower*, it is bent *towards* the normal (as in part b).

(d) In Figure 27 the angle of refraction is *smaller* than the angle of incidence—the wave is bent towards the normal—so that the situation resembles that in part b in which the magnitude of the velocity (the speed) v_1 is greater than v_2.

ITQ 15 Using Snell's law:

$$\dfrac{\sin i}{\sin r} = \dfrac{v_1}{v_2} \qquad (12)*$$

In this case

$$\dfrac{\sin i}{\sin 90°} = \dfrac{1}{1.5}$$

Because $\sin 90° = 1$,

$$\sin i = 1/1.5$$

$$= 0.6667$$

The angle of incidence is therefore 41.8°.

ITQ 16 You should have noticed that there is a much greater density of iron filings at the two ends of the magnet than elsewhere. There should be relatively few filings at the sides of the magnet but those that do occur should form part of a continuous curved pattern of filings that seems to focus on the two ends. You should also notice that the filings at the sides tend to be flat on the paper, parallel to the sides of the magnet, whereas those at the ends lie in different orientations, many of them sticking out of the paper.

ITQ 17 (a) The arrows should point *away* from the points X and Y, along the curves towards the south pole of the magnet. This is because, as we have already discussed, the arrows on field lines mark the direction along which the north pole of a compass needle points.

(b) No, the angles made with the circle by the two curves are not the same. The angle varies according to where the curves cut the circle. You can see two sets of possibilities in Figure 80. The field lines passing through points X and X' cut the circle more obliquely than those passing through Y and Y'.

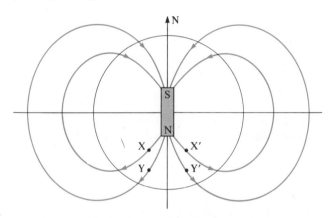

FIGURE 80 The results of Experiment 2 showing the magnetic field lines around a bar magnet and the way they cut a surrounding circle (for ITQs 17 and 18).

ITQ 18 No, the field direction will change according to position on the sphere. Above the poles of the magnet, the field lines will be perpendicular to the surface of the sphere. Half-way between the top and the bottom, the field lines will be parallel to the surface. In fact, the field lines through all cross-sections of the sphere which pass through the top and bottom points will look like Figure 80.

ITQ 19 (a) The lowest values of magnetic field strength occur over South America (24 000 nT), spreading out into an approximately east–west elongated zone around and to the south of the Equator. The highest values of magnetic field strength occur near Antarctica, along the 60° S line of latitude and exceed 66 000 nT. High values also occur in northerly latitudes, around 60° N, where they exceed 60 000 nT in two places, one over the Hudson Bay area (around 90° W longitude) and the other over the USSR and China (around 100° E longitude).

(b) In *broad terms*, the dipole model is supported because the general north–south variation of magnetic field strength resembles the theoretical model in Figure

47. But a simple dipole would give a more regular pattern with contours more nearly parallel to the magnetic equator than appear in Figure 46. In particular, the roughly circular magnetic low over eastern South America and the adjacent Atlantic, and the high over central USSR would not be present if the Earth's field were a simple dipole.

ITQ 20 (a) The flints appear to lose their magnetism as they are heated; above a certain temperature, they cannot be picked up with a magnet.

(b) Their magnetism 'reappears' when they are cooled.

ITQ 21 38 minutes (P-waves); 64 minutes (S-waves).

This is simply a case of dividing the distance by the speed to find the time taken. Remember from Unit 3 that:

$$\text{speed} = \frac{\text{distance}}{\text{time}}$$

so that

$$\text{time} = \frac{\text{distance}}{\text{speed}}$$

Thus for P-waves,

$$\text{time} = \frac{12\,740 \times 10^3 \text{ m}}{5.6 \times 10^3 \text{ m s}^{-1}}$$

$$\approx 2\,300 \text{ seconds}$$

$$\approx 38 \text{ minutes}$$

Using a similar calculation, we can show that S-waves take about 64 minutes.

ITQ 22 If the position of an earthquake makes no difference to travel times to particular epicentral angles, then the Earth must be *radially symmetrical*. This means that at all points at a given distance from the centre of the Earth, the seismic properties of the materials of the interior are the same. In other words, the variations in seismic properties are concentrically arranged. If the core were offset from the centre then, assuming that it has some effect on wave speeds, waves of the *same epicentral angle* that passed through more of the core than others would be more affected by the change in speed.

ITQ 23 The wave will undergo *continuous refraction* (see Figures 32–34) and will eventually return to the surface at an angle of 25° to the horizontal. (You should re-read the relevant parts of Section 2.5 if you found this question difficult.)

ITQ 24 (a) The absence of S-waves at epicentral angles greater than 103° (Figure 54) indicates that there is *liquid* beneath 2 900 km depth (Figure 55a) in the Earth. Moreover, P-waves travel at *reduced speeds* through the core, compared with the mantle: this is indicated by the greater P-wave travel times beyond 142° (Figure 54) and by the existence of a P-wave shadow zone (103°–142°) which implies refraction *towards the normal* (Figure 55b) into a zone of lower wave speed.

(b) The density of the core must be much *greater* than the Earth's average density ($5.5 \times 10^3 \text{ kg m}^{-3}$) because the most dense mantle rocks ($5.4 \times 10^3 \text{ kg m}^{-3}$) are *less dense* than the Earth's average density. (Of course, the average density of the mantle is much less than $5.4 \times 10^3 \, \text{kg m}^{-3}$.)

(c) The increase in density alone across the core–mantle boundary might be enough to explain the observed decrease in P-wave speeds from the equation:

$$v_P = \sqrt{\psi/\rho} \qquad (9)*$$

But, given that the outer core is liquid and that liquids are more compressible than solids, the axial modulus ψ in the outermost core may well be less than in the lower mantle which would further reduce P-wave speeds. (Do not worry if this is an elusive point—we consider it again in the text following ITQ 24 and in Section 4.4.2.)

(d) The secular variation of the Earth's magnetic field, discussed in Section 3.4.3, combined with the fact that the deep interior of the Earth must be above the Curie temperature for permanently magnetic material, both suggest that the field must originate in a *liquid* layer that is in a dynamic state.

ITQ 25   (a) $8.1 \, \text{km s}^{-1}$.

Snell's law tells us that

$$\frac{\sin i}{\sin r} = \frac{v_1}{v_2} \qquad (12)*$$

Substituting for i, r and v_1, we have

$$\frac{\sin 90°}{\sin 36.6°} = \frac{13.6}{v_2} \, \text{km s}^{-1}$$

Therefore

$$v_2 = \left(\frac{13.6 \sin 36.6°}{\sin 90°} \right) \text{km s}^{-1}$$

$$= 8.1 \, \text{km s}^{-1} \text{ (to 2 significant figures)}$$

i.e. the speed of P-waves in the outermost core is $8.1 \, \text{km s}^{-1}$.

(b) $18.5°$.

Using Snell's law again, this time to find the angle of refraction:

$$\frac{\sin 42°}{\sin r} = \frac{13.6}{8.1}$$

Therefore

$$\sin r = \frac{8.1 \sin 42°}{13.6}$$

$$= 0.3985$$

whence $r = 23.48°$

$$= 23.5° \text{ (to 3 significant figures)}$$

Since $i = 42°$, this wave is bent by $(42 - 23.5)° = 18.5°$.

ITQ 26   The outer core has a density of $9.9 \times 10^3 \, \text{kg m}^{-3}$ which is less than that of liquid iron. So we must conclude that some material *less dense* than liquid iron is also present in the outer core. This could not be nickel because this metal it is even more dense than iron (see text preceding ITQ 26).

ITQ 27   Two possible explanations are that the magnetic poles have moved relative to the geographic poles, or that the *continents* have moved relative to the geographic poles (and therefore by implication relative to the magnetic poles as well).

ITQ 28   If the paths have the same shape, then the two continents must have moved in exactly the same way. Such a coincidence seems very unlikely unless the two continents were actually joined together from 400–100 Ma ago.

ITQ 29   Because iron is a strongly magnetic material, one way would involve flying several parallel traverses over the area with a compass-like instrument which records the strength of the Earth's magnetic field combined with that due to the rocks.

ITQ 30   Because oil (and, for that matter, natural gas) is lighter than water, it will tend to float and so migrate to higher levels. If it is trapped in a dome such as this, the oil-bearing sediments can be tapped by drilling.

ITQ 31   For earthquakes, some seismometers will receive upward motions and some downward, corresponding to the quadrants of Figure 74b. First motions for explosions will always be upwards.

ITQ 32   (a) We can be almost certain that Britain will not suffer a major earthquake, because we do not live in the seismic zones shown on Figure 13 and we can be fairly sure from oral and written history that there has not been an earthquake of that magnitude in the last 1 000 years (since the Norman Conquest).

(b) China may well suffer a great earthquake as, on the evidence of seismic zones and the past record (Figure 13 and Table 3, in Section 1), they occur fairly regularly.

ITQ 33   The rocks here are continuously but slowly creeping past each other; there are no earthquakes because there are no sudden jerky releases of accumulated strain. You might like to write 'creeping' along Section II of the SAFS in Figure 77.

SAQ ANSWERS AND COMMENTS

SAQ 1

	Mercalli	Richter
(a) It measures the magnitude of an earthquake.	×	✓
(b) It measures the intensity of an earthquake	✓	×
(c) It has a maximum value of ten.	×	×
(d) It is a measure of the maximum amount of ground movement.	×	✓

Statements (a) and (b) are the definitions of the two terms—see text.

(c) The Mercalli scale has 12 points (Table 2) and the Richter scale is open-ended.

(d) See Section 1.7.

SAQ 2 Figure 17a shows a fence twisted into a sinuous shape, which is probably the result of compression and shearing (see Figures 11b and c). This fence was photographed in Montana following an earthquake in August 1959 with epicentre near the junction of Montana, Wyoming and Idaho. The earthquake had a magnitude of 7.1. Figure 17b shows a fence that has been offset by 2–3 m, by shearing motion (see Figure 11c); this picture is an illustration of the movement on the San Andreas Fault during the San Francisco earthquake in 1906.

SAQ 4 (a) The focus of an earthquake is defined as the point of initial slip or first movement of a fault at the beginning of the earthquake.

(b) The epicentre of an earthquake is defined as the point on the Earth's surface directly (vertically) above the focus of the earthquake.
Figure 10 shows the positions of the focus and the epicentre of an earthquake.

SAQ 5 (c) True. Figure 13 shows that a great number of earthquakes originate in the crust beneath the oceans.

(a) Not true. 'Major' or 'great' earthquakes are largely restricted to seismic zones (Figure 13).

(b) Not true. Earthquakes can happen in the same places twice. One tragic case was the destruction of the city of Agadir, Morocco, on 29 February 1960, which had previously been wrecked by an earthquake in 1751. Lisbon has also suffered two major earthquakes—in 1531 and 1755.

SAQ 6 (a) Statements (ii) and (iii) are correct (see below).

(b) Statement (ii) correctly explains why S-waves do not pass through liquids.

(i) and (v) Liquids are difficult to compress and have 'normal' values of axial modulus rather than very low values. (In fact, axial moduli are lower in liquids than in solids.) Thus (i) and (v) are incorrect.

(ii) and (iv) Liquids have no resistance to shear deformation; hence (iv) the rigidity modulus is zero, and v_S is zero. Thus (ii) is correct and is also the correct explanation for part (b); (iv) is incorrect.

(iii) Since density is mass divided by volume, when the volume of a given mass of substance is reduced by compression, the density must increase. So (iii) is correct but is not the correct explanation for part (b).

SAQ 7 $v_P = 5.6\,\text{km s}^{-1}$; $v_S = 3.3\,\text{km s}^{-1}$.

Using the equation:

$$v_P = \sqrt{\frac{\psi}{\rho}} \qquad (9)^*$$

and substituting the values given for ψ and ρ, we have

$$v_P = \sqrt{\frac{8.5 \times 10^{10}\,\text{N m}^{-2}}{2.7 \times 10^3\,\text{kg m}^{-3}}}$$

$$= 5.6 \times 10^3\,\text{m s}^{-1}$$

So P-waves travel with a speed of $5.6\,\text{km s}^{-1}$.

Using the equation:

$$v_S = \sqrt{\frac{\mu}{\rho}} \qquad (11)^*$$

and substituting for μ and ρ:

$$v_S = \sqrt{\frac{3.0 \times 10^{10}\,\text{N m}^{-2}}{2.7 \times 10^3\,\text{kg m}^{-3}}}$$

$$= 3.3 \times 10^3\,\text{m s}^{-1}$$

So S-waves travel with a speed of $3.3\,\text{km s}^{-1}$.

SAQ 8 The correct statements are (b) and (c).

We use the general relationship:

$$\text{wave speed} = \sqrt{\text{elastic modulus/density}}$$

(of which Equations 9 and 11 are specific forms).

SAQ 3

Characteristics of rock hand specimens S1, S3, S4 and S6.

Specimen	Interlocking crystals?	Rounded grains?	Size of crystals or grains	Igneous or sedimentary
S1 granite	yes, 3 different minerals present	no	large, up to 4–5 mm	igneous
S3 basalt	yes	no	small, up to 1 mm	igneous
S4 peridotite	yes	no	large, up to 3 mm	igneous
S6 sandstone	no, cemented	yes, clearly	1–2 mm, some variation	sedimentary

Check back to the AV sequence and Table 1 if you had any difficulty with this question.

It follows that wave speed will increase if elastic modulus alone increases—so (b) is correct, and (d) is incorrect. Also, wave speed increases if density alone *decreases*—so (a) is incorrect and (c) is correct. (e) would be a correct statement about the *increase* of P- and S-wave speeds: both would increase if elastic modulus increased faster than density.

SAQ 9   41°.

This question requires the application of Snell's law:

$$\frac{\sin i}{\sin r} = \frac{v_1}{v_2} \qquad (12)^*$$

so

$$\frac{\sin 30°}{\sin r} = \frac{6.3}{8.2}$$

Therefore

$$6.3 \times \sin r = 8.2 \times \sin 30°$$

$$= 8.2 \times 0.5$$

so

$$\sin r = \frac{8.2 \times 0.5}{6.3} = 0.65$$

Thus $r = 41°$.

SAQ 10   (d) is correct—see Equation 13; all the other equations are incorrect.

SAQ 11   It will only be reflected.

The wave will be reflected if the angle of incidence is greater than the critical angle i_c (see Figures 29–31), which is given by the equation:

$$\sin i_c = \frac{v_1}{v_2}. \qquad (14)^*$$

In this case

$$\sin i_c = \frac{4.5}{5.5}$$

$$= 0.8182$$

so $i_c = 55°$

It follows that a wave arriving at the boundary at an incident angle of 60° will be totally reflected and will not be refracted (as in Figure 31).

SAQ 12   The wave path will show the changes in curvature illustrated in Figure 36 only if wave speed *decreases* with depth in layer A and then *increases* with depth in layer B. (Compare Figure 36 with Figure 33 and study the associated text if you had any difficulty with this question.)

SAQ 13   (c) is correct–see Section 3.2; (e) is correct—as proved (we hope!) in Experiment 3.
(a) is incorrect—the force is repulsive; (b) is incorrect—see Section 3.2; (d) is incorrect—as pointed out in Section 3.2, the end of a compass needle which points towards the magnetic pole (M_N) in the Earth's Northern Hemisphere is defined as the north pole.

SAQ 14   (a) is correct.

Examination of Figures 40 and 44 and the associated text should prove to you that (a) is correct and (b) is incorrect. For (c), note that the north pole of a bar magnet will be attracted *along* the direction of the field lines where the magnet is situated, which will not usually be directly towards the poles of the dipole, because of the curved shape of the field lines.

SAQ 15   (a) The average strength of the Earth's field as measured at the geomagnetic equator has varied by a factor of about 3 (Figure 51) over the last 10^4 years. The variations have been cyclic with maxima 9000 and 1500 years ago and a minimum about 5500 years ago. At present the field strength at the geomagnetic equator is declining and it appears that a complete cycle takes almost 10^4 years (in fact about 7000–8000 years).

(b) The Earth's magnetic axis wobbles about its axis of rotation, never being more than about 11° from this axis (Figure 50). The wobble also appears to have a period of the order of 10^4 years.

SAQ 16   The non-dipole component of the Earth's magnetic field is that part of the Earth's total magnetic field which remains after the geomagnetic dipole field has been deducted from the measured field. The positions of the highs and lows in the non-dipole field, together with the strength of the field, vary substantially on a time-scale of between 10 and 10^3 years. For example, the highs and lows shown in Figure 48a had drifted to the west during the 150 years since Figure 48b was compiled.

SAQ 17   (a) True. This is simply the definition of the term 'axial'.

(b) False. At present the geomagnetic dipole is inclined at about 11° to the rotation axis.

(c) True. The dipole axis cuts the Earth's surface at antipodal points (see Figures 38 and 46); that is, they lie at opposite ends of an Earth diameter.

(d) False. At the geomagnetic pole M_N the inclination of the *dipole* field is 90°. But at this point the irregular non-dipole field is not zero, and so the resultant inclination differs from 90°. The true position of $+90°$ inclination is the dip pole P_N in Figure 46.

(e) True. The strength of the dipole field varies from just over 30000 nT at the geomagnetic equator to just over 60000 nT at the geomagnetic poles (Figures 46 and 47).

(f) False. The magnetic dip poles are the points on the Earth's surface at which the inclination produced by the dipole and non-dipole fields acting together is either $+90°$ (north magnetic dip pole) or $-90°$ (south magnetic dip pole). These points are not antipodal because the non-dipole field is irregular.

(g) False. The geomagnetic poles (M_N and M_S) are inverted with respect to the geographic poles (Section 3.2). In other words, the *south magnetic* pole of the imaginary dipole is closer to the *north geographic* pole of the Earth.

SAQ 18 The three features (see Section 3.4) are:

(a) the rapid rate of change of the non-dipole field component;

(b) the slower rate of change of the dipole field strength and pole positions; and

(c) the fact that in the deep interior of the Earth, where the field appears to originate, the temperature of the rocks must be higher than the Curie temperature for all known materials—thus it appears that there cannot be a permanent (solid) magnet deep inside the Earth.

SAQ 19 The correct reasons are (a) and (d)—see Section 4.3.

(b) is incorrect. As we have pointed out several times in this double Unit (e.g. Section 1.2) boreholes have not been able to penetrate more than a few kilometres beneath the surface; therefore, they have not reached the mantle. (An attempt was made in 1957 to drill through the oceanic crust—the Mohole project—but this had to be abandoned because of technical difficulties.)

(c) is incorrect. Although peridotite is exposed in many places, it has been detached from the mantle by major Earth movements and is not 'in place'.

SAQ 20 The relationship between epicentral angle and travel times for seismic waves from an earthquake is independent of the geographical position of the earthquake. The only way that the variations in the Earth's seismic properties can be arranged, so that this is the case, is for the variations to be determined by the distance from the Earth's centre, or in other words, to be radially symmetric (see Sections 4.1 and 4.2).

SAQ 21 (a) Phase changes are by far the most important (see Section 4.3). The whole of the mantle is thought to be essentially homogeneous and to have the chemical composition of peridotite. The variations in seismic wave properties observed must therefore be due to phase changes in the peridotite.

(b) In the low-speed zone (which occurs between 50 and 250 km depth), up to 5% of the material is liquid as a result of partial melting of the lower-melting temperature components of the peridotite. Between 400 and 1 050 km, there are three phase changes in which the peridotite changes to higher pressure (and therefore denser) forms of peridotite. This 650 km thick layer is known as the transition zone (see Figures 56 and 57).

SAQ 22 P-waves from an earthquake focus which travel down into the Earth are continuously refracted away from the normal as they descend because the P-wave speed is continuously increasing with depth. The wave that reaches an epicentral angle of 103° has penetrated to a depth of 2 900 km (see Figure 55). Waves that penetrate below that depth meet the core–mantle boundary, and are strongly refracted into the core, resulting in the absence of P-wave arrivals beyond 103°. For waves that meet the boundary at angles of incidence of less than 42°, the geometry of the wave paths is such that they emerge at epicentral angles of greater than 142° (see Figure 62 and associated text).

SAQ 23 (c) and (d) are correct—see Section 4.2 and Figures 55 and 62.

There is no evidence of P- or S-wave arrivals at epicentral angles which would fit with the proposition that these waves are completely reflected at the core–mantle boundary so (a) and (e) are incorrect.

(b) is the opposite of the correct answer (c): because P-wave speed drops as the waves enter the core, the waves must be refracted towards the normal (i.e. into the core).

(f) is the opposite of what happens—if it were correct then the waves would be refracted away from the normal and there would be no P-wave shadow zone.

SAQ 24 The Earth's magnetic field is thought to be produced by a series of electric current loops (as in a solenoid—Figure 59) moving in a helical pattern (see Figure 60) within the liquid outer core. This is largely made of iron and so is electrically conducting. The fact that the currents are flowing produces a field, and convective movement of the liquid outer core material results in the production of further electric currents in the moving material, which themselves generate a magnetic field. This is the self-exciting dynamo (see Figure 61). The pattern of the induced electric currents is such that the resulting magnetic field is dipolar.

SAQ 25 (a) Since there are no S-wave arrivals beyond epicentral angles of 103°, S-waves which have penetrated deeper than 2 900 km are not being transmitted beneath that depth. Only a liquid can account for this, since the rigidity modulus for a liquid is zero, and the S-wave speed is therefore also zero (see Section 4.2).

(b) (The evidence is dealt with in Section 4.4.3):

(i) The outer core at least must be an electrically conducting material, to account for Earth's magnetic field.

(ii) Iron with appropriate mixtures of sulphur for the outer core and nickel for the inner core has the seismic properties that are required to account for the seismic observations.

(iii) Results of experiments at very high temperatures and pressures indicate that iron with sulphur and nickel has the required physical properties.

(iv) The compositions of iron meteorites and the relative abundance of likely metals in the Solar System both point to the core composition which is suggested.

SAQ 26 Figure 81 (overleaf) is a completed version of Figure 67. Listen again to the second AV sequence if you had any difficulty with this question.

SAQ 27 The fact that all the rocks of a particular age have either reversed or normal magnetization, regardless of rock type or of location, shows that field reversals have taken place. For example, all basalts of a given age have normal magnetization, whilst otherwise identical basalts of a different age have reversed magnetization.

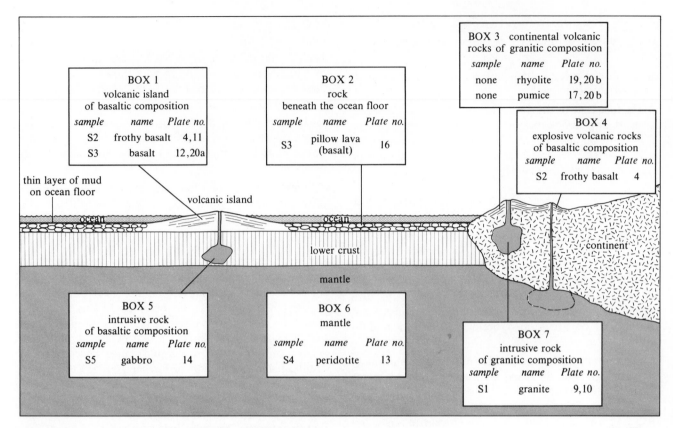

FIGURE 81   Completed version of Figure 67 (for SAQ 26).

SAQ 28   Apparent polar wandering paths are produced by plotting on world maps the apparent positions of the Earth's magnetic poles as deduced from the magnetic inclination of rocks of different ages from particular parts of continents. Because the apparent polar wandering paths are of different shapes for different continents, the continents *must* have changed their positions relative to the Earth's geographic poles, assuming that the geographic and magnetic poles are coincident. This is true to a first approximation (see Figure 50).

SAQ 29   Because we must move the continental outlines along with the apparent polar wandering paths when fitting the paths together, we can deduce the way the continents fitted together during the times when the paths coincide i.e. during the times when the continents 'shared' the same magnetic poles.

SAQ 30   In 40 million years!

2 cm movement in 1 year corresponds to 1 metre (100 cm) movement in 50 years,

i.e. to 1 km in (50 × 1 000) years = 50 000 years

So for 800 km

time = 800 × 50 000 years = 40 Ma

As you will see in later Earth science Units, this is not a long time in geological terms.

INDEX FOR UNITS 5–6

ACKNOWLEDGEMENTS

Grateful acknowledgement is made to the following sources for material used in this double Unit:

Figure 1 Rex Features/SIPA—Press/Photographer: Novedades; *Figure 7* UPI/Bettmann Newsphotos; *Figure 8* Albert Moldvay, California; *Figure 9* Dr George Housner, California Institute of Technology; *Figure 17a* US Geological Survey, Denver, Colorado/J. R. Stacy; *Figure 17b* US Geological Survey, Menlo Park, California; *Figure 48* Dr D. R. Barraclough, Geomagnetism Research Group, British Geological Survey. *Figure 73b* Petty Geophysical Engineering Co. from M. Press and R. Siever (1982) *Earth*, 3rd edn, W. H. Freeman and Co.

Plate 1 NASA; *Plates 2a and 2b* John S. Shelton, California; *Plate 6* Reproduced by permission of the Director, British Geological Survey: Crown Copyright reserved; *Plate 8b* British Museum (Natural History) Geological Museum, London.

Table 3b Global Seismology Research Group of the British Geological Survey, Edinburgh.